Spelling Connections 4

Louis Quildon

NELSON CANADA

© Nelson Canada,
A Division of International Thomson Limited, 1987

All rights in this book are reserved

Published in 1987 by
Nelson Canada,
A Division of International Thomson Limited
1120 Birchmount Road
Scarborough, Ontario
M1K 5G4

ISBN 0-17-602291-0

Canadian Cataloguing in Publication Data

Quildon, Louis.
  Spelling Connections 4

For use in schools.
ISBN 0-17-602291-0

I. Spellers. 2. English language - Spelling and
orthography - Problems, exercises, etc. I. Title.

PE1145.2.Q56 1987   428.1   C86-094096-9

Contributing Author: Elma Schemenauer
Project Manager: Alan Simpson
Editor: Terry-Lee Wheelband
Series Design: Mary Jane Gerber
Design and Art Direction: Sharon Foster
Cover Design: Mary Jane Gerber
Cover Illustration: Barry Carlton and Elva Hook
Cover Photography: Jeremy Jones
Typesetting: Trigraph Inc.
Printing: The Bryant Press Ltd.

Illustrations:
Darlene Burgess: 19 (lower), 26, 32, 33 (upper), 74 (upper), 103, 114, 120 (lower),
121 (lower), 148, 149; Heather Collins: 136; Mark Craig: 69, 131, 135; Sally
Davies: 40, 59, 61, 86, 94, 95, 133, 143; Susanna Denti: 38 (upper) 67, 89
(lower), 102, 107-109; Sharon Foster: 78, 80 (lower), 91, 93; Blake Foy: 24
(lower), 25, 51, 70, 79, 101, 115, 138 (lower), 140, 142, 144; Don Gauthier: 15,
17, 32 (upper), 33 (lower), 88, 89 (upper), 128, 145; Mary Jane Gerber: 97, 98
(upper), 99; Heather Graham: 10, 11, 53, 55, 72, 74 (lower), 116; Frank
Hammond: 81, 83, 134, 137, 146; Katherine Helmur: 37, 38 (border), 39 (border);
Rob Johannsen: 43-45; Nancy Kettles: 12, 14, 113; Vesna Krstanovich: 62;
Vladyana Krykorka: 34, 36, 56, 57; Sharon Matthews: 24 (upper), 110, 112, 119,
120 (upper); Wayne McKenzie: 50, 52 (upper); Glenn Mielke: 21-23, 126, 127;
David Shaw: 28, 30, 47, 49, 65, 66, 68, 84, 85, 87, 104-106, 122-125; Lisa Smith:
18, 19 (upper), 20, 75, 77, 100, 150; Lorraine Tuson: 141; Tracy Walker: 13, 35,
38 (lower), 52 (lower), 63, 71, 80 (upper), 82, 92, 96, 98 (lower), 138 (upper), 147.

Acknowledgements:
Team logos used by permission of: Toronto Maple Leaf Hockey Club, Calgary
Flames Hockey Club, Vancouver Canucks Hockey Club.

Excerpt from *Mice at Centre Ice* by Estelle Salata. Used by permission of the
author. Published by Nelson Canada, 1984.

Printed and bound in Canada
    67890/BP/65432

Table of Contents

4

6

Handwriting Models

Aa Bb Cc Dd

Ee Ff Gg Hh

Ii Jj Kk Ll

Mm Nn Oo Pp

Qq Rr Ss Tt

Uu Vv Ww Xx

Yy Zz 1 2 3 4 5 6 7 8 9 0

Print Models

Aa Bb Cc Dd

Ee Ff Gg Hh

Ii Jj Kk Ll

Mm Nn Oo Pp

Qq Rr Ss Tt

Uu Vv Ww Xx

Yy Zz

How to Use This Book

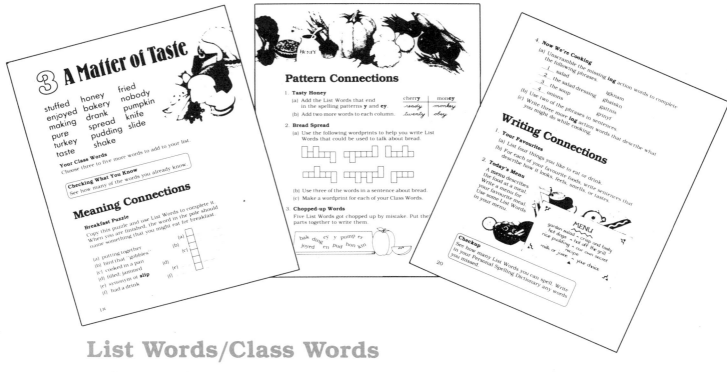

List Words/Class Words

Before you begin each Unit, take time to talk about the theme. Talk about the List Words. Add some other theme words that you and your class would like to learn to spell. These are Your Class Words.

Checking What You Know

Here you will find out which List Words and Class Words you can already spell. You will also find out which parts of words are problems for you.

Meaning Connections

Before you can use a word, you need to know what it means. In this section you will choose the best List Words to complete stories and poems. You will find out that some words can have many meanings. You will also discover words that mean almost the same as other words, and words that are opposites.

Pattern Connections

Many words have families—just like people. In this section you will discover families of words where some of the sounds are the same but are spelled differently. You will also find words that share the same pattern of letters. Knowing about word families will help you spell the many new words you will meet in school and at home.

Writing Connections

This section will give you a chance to use the words you have learned. You will be writing about how you feel and what you know. You may write a poem, a story, or sentences.

Checkup

At the end of the Unit you will see how many more List Words and Class Words you can now spell. You will also see which words are still giving you problems. Collect these problem words in your **Personal Spelling Dictionary** to help you with your writing.

Backup

Every sixth Unit is a special review Unit called **Backup**. You will be looking back at the List Words and using them to play games, and to solve riddles and puzzles.

Wordworks

Spelling is fun because learning new words helps you think of new ideas. The **Wordworks** page in each Backup Unit gives you a chance to write about interesting things in new ways.

Superconnections

There are some exciting word games and challenges in the back of this book. Find out more about words and make your writing power grow. Your teacher will show you which activities are just for *you*.

Spelling Is for Writing

Why is it important to spell correctly?

When is it important to spell correctly?

Share your ideas with your classmates.

Help Yourself with These Study Steps

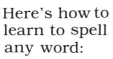

Here's how to learn to spell any word:

STEP 1, Look and Study

Look carefully at the word. Say it to yourself. See how its sounds are spelled.

STEP 2, Picture

THEIRS

Picture the word in your mind.

STEP 3, Write and Check

Now look away from the word. Write the word. Look back at the word to see if you spelled it correctly.

If you still need help, go back to Step 1.

1 Let's Go Camping

net
hike
camping
rod
sitting
tent
rowing
God
stones

cabin
country
lake
standing
September
alone
cold
water

Your Class Words

Add three to five words your class would like to spell.

> **Checking What You Know**
> The Study Steps will help you spell any words
> you missed on the Pretest.

Meaning Connections

The Joys of Camping

Write the List Words that complete the following story:

   In S__1__, when the leaves turn gold, we go c__2__ in
the c__3__. We stay in an old, wooden c__4__ by the lake.
We swim and play and laugh. Sometimes, we take a
fishing r__5__ and go fishing.

   Once my sister and I went on a h__6__ along a trail by

the l__7__ shore. We found some flat, white s__8__. When we turned one stone over, a tiny black cricket scurried away. "Leave me a__9__!" the little cricket seemed to say.

Pattern Connections

1. **Footprints, Wordprints**

   (a) A footprint shows the shape of a foot. A **wordprint** shows the shape of a word. Like this:

   Copy these wordprints and write a List Word for each.

   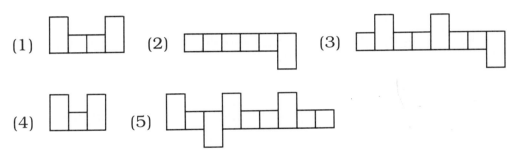

   (b) Make a wordprint for each of your Class Words.

2. **Pitching Tents**

   We can add ing to some words. For example:

   help—helping   We call help a **root word**.

   (a) If help is the root word of helping, what is the root word of swimming?

   (b) Add ing to each word and write it in the tent where it belongs.

stand	camp	row	sit
hike	net	water	tent

   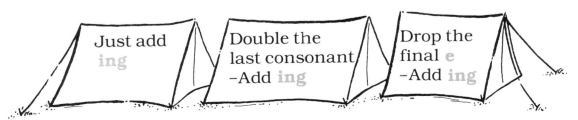

   Just add ing

   Double the last consonant –Add ing

   Drop the final e –Add ing

3. **Open-air o's**

Many words have the **long o** sound as in **open**. We spell this sound in several different ways:

o	ow	o_e
gold	grow	rose
ocean	snowflake	pole

(a) Find the List Words that have this o sound and write them under the correct spelling patterns.

(b) To complete the chart, add two more outdoor words of your own to each column.

(c) Write two sentences about the outdoors that use words from your chart.

Writing Connections

1. **Cool Stones**

Stones are often cool. Name four more outdoor things that could be cool.

2. **If I Could Go Camping...**

What kind of camping trip would you like to take? Write a story to tell about your trip. Where would you like to go and who would you like to go with? What might you see, touch, hear, smell, or taste there?

▶ Give your story a title, then read it carefully to check your spelling and your use of capitals and punctuation marks.

Checkup
See how many List Words you can spell now.

2 *Far Side of the Moon*

safe   space
path   living
life   hunting
shaped   lift-off
Mars   pushed
float   rocket
forms   there
being   earth
passed

Your Class Words
Choose three more words
to add to your list.

Checking What You Know
How many of the words can you already spell?

Meaning Connections

1. **Anyone for Mars**?

   Words that have almost the same meanings are called
   synonyms. Write the List Words that are synonyms for
   the words printed like this in the story.

   "Get set for take-off," a steady voice called from the
   control room. 10-9-8-7... After ten seconds, the ASTRA
   II blasted off. Its powerful rocket, formed like a bullet,

continued on the next page...   15

thrust the spaceship away from the earth into outer space.

    The astronauts were relaxed. They knew the ASTRA II was on the right **route** and that they would be **unharmed**. They wondered what they would find on Mars.

    "What will happen when we go **looking** for information about the planet? Will we find any **kinds** of life there?"

2. **Blasting Off with Synonyms**

    (a) A **thesaurus** lists words with their synonyms. Words in a thesaurus are in alphabetical order. Write the following List Words in alphabetical order:

       path   safe   forms   living

       pushed   float   passed   hunting

    (b) Use the Mini-Thesaurus in the back of this book. Find and write a synonym for each List Word you just wrote.

Pattern Connections

1. **Crossing Space Rhymes**

    (a) Draw shapes like the ones below. Add letters to make crossword pairs that rhyme. (**Hint:** One word in each pair is a List Word.)

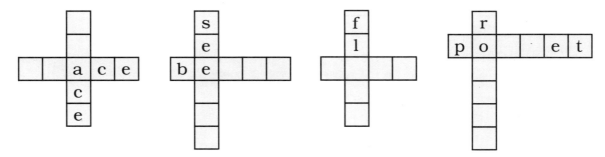

    (b) Write two sentences about space that use the words in two of your crossword pairs.

2. **Earth to Mars**

    Write in alphabetical order the List Words with **r** in them.

3. Journey into Endless Space

form life
shape path
less

(a) If **fearless** means "without fear," what does **endless** mean? Use the spaceship to write four **less** words.

(b) Add two more **less** words to your list.

(c) Use three **less** words from your list in three sentences about space travel.

Writing Connections

1. Adding Space Details

The following sentence doesn't tell much:

I met a creature.

By adding details, we can make it more interesting.

On my way to school I met a **lonesome space** creature **that came from a faraway planet**.

Make these sentences more interesting by adding details:

(a) The rocket left.

(c) The astronauts explored.

(b) The spaceship landed.

(d) They found life.

2. Your Space Creature

Pretend you have met a creature from outer space. Write a story to tell about your space creature. What is its name? What does it look like? How does it move around? Does it have special powers? Give your story an interesting title.

> ### Checkup
> Add any words you need to study to your Personal Spelling Dictionary.

3 A Matter of Taste

stuffed   honey   fried
enjoyed   bakery   nobody
making   drank   pumpkin
pure   spread   knife
turkey   pudding   slide
taste   shake

Your Class Words

Choose three to five more words to add to your list.

> **Checking What You Know**
> See how many of the words you already know.

Meaning Connections

Breakfast Puzzle

Copy this puzzle and use List Words to complete it.
When you are finished, the word in the pole should
name something that you might eat for breakfast.

(a) putting together

(b) bird that "gobbles"

(c) cooked in a pan

(d) filled; jammed

(e) synonym of slip

(f) had a drink

(a) ☐ _ _ _ _ _

(b) _ ☐ _ _ _ _

(c) ☐ _ _ _ _

(d) _ _ _ ☐ _ _ _

(e) _ _ ☐ _ _

(f) _ _ _ ☐ _

Pattern Connections

1. **Tasty Honey**

   (a) Add the List Words that end in the spelling patterns **y** and **ey**.

   (b) Add two more words to each column.

cherr**y**	mon**ey**
ready	*monkey*
twenty	*obey*

2. **Bread Spread**

   (a) Use the following wordprints to help you write List Words that could be used to talk about bread.

   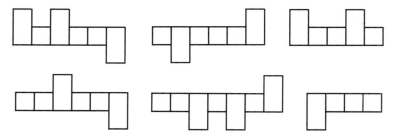

   (b) Use three of the words in a sentence about bread.

   (c) Make a wordprint for each of your Class Words.

3. **Chopped-up Words**

   Five List Words got chopped up by mistake. Put their parts together to write them.

   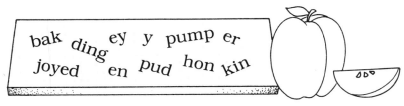

bak ding ey y pump er joyed en pud hon kin

Fun

4. Now We're Cooking

(a) Unscramble the missing **ing** action words to complete the following phrases.

__1__	salad	igknam
__2__	the salad dressing	ghaiskn
__3__	the soup	gattnis
__4__	onions	grinyf

(b) Use two of the phrases in sentences.

(c) Write three more **ing** action words that describe what you might do while cooking.

Writing Connections

1. Your Favourites

(a) List four things you like to eat or drink.

(b) For each of your favourite foods, write sentences that describe how it looks, feels, smells, or tastes.

2. Today's Menu

A **menu** describes the food at a meal. Write a menu for your favourite meal. Use some List Words in your menu.

MENU

garden salad ∧ crisp and tasty
hot dogs ∧ hot off the grill
rice pudding ∧ our own secret recipe
milk or juice ∧ your choice

Checkup

See how many List Words you can spell. Write in your Personal Spelling Dictionary any words you missed.

4 Weather Watch

clear   heat   warm   snowflake
clouds   during   weather   falling
storm   fair   thunder   blow
shine   sunny   October   wind
rained

Your Class Words

Add more words your class would like to spell.

Checking What You Know

The Study Steps will help you spell the words you missed.

Meaning Connections

And Now the Weather

What words does a weather forecaster use? Write the List Words that belong in these groups. (**Hint**: Some List Words could be used in more than one group.)

Words to tell what the weather is like
hot, cold ...

Action words to use in a weather report
freeze, snowing ...

Words naming things that make up the weather
lightning, breeze ...

21

Pattern Connections

1. **Weather Compounds**

   (a) *I see a snowflake on your jacket.*

   Which word in the sentence
   was made by joining two words?

   Put these words together
   to write six new weather
   words:

   > fall sun
   > clouds   wind
   > rain
   >   thunder
   > shine
   >   storm snow

   (b) Use some of your
   new words to write
   two sentences about weather.

2. **Tongue Twister Time**

   (a) How quickly can you say this tongue twister?

   On a **cl**ear **cr**isp day, the **cl**ouds aren't **cl**ose.

   Write another weather tongue twister using words
   that begin with **cl** and **cr**.

   (b) Find and write the sixteen words beginning with two
   consonants in the following story.

   Gray clouds floated across a blackening sky. The
   wind began to blow. Soon the storm turned into a
   blizzard.

   In our trailer we stayed snug and warm. At last the
   wind stopped. We opened the door and ran out to play
   in the fresh clean snow.

   (c) Choose one of the consonant patterns. Write a tongue
   twister using four or five words that begin with that
   pattern.

3. **Snowflake Scramble**

Unscramble the letters in the snowflakes to write
six List Words.

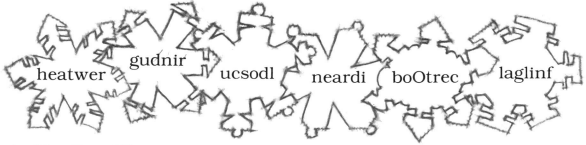

heatwer   gudnir   ucsodl   neardi   boOtrec   laglinf

4. **Weather Y's**

Notice how these words change when y is added:

mist—*misty*   fog—*foggy*   ice—*icy*

Add y to these words and write the new words you
make.

storm	rain	sun	chill	gust
shine	wind	breeze	mud	snow

Writing Connections

1. **Snow Bound**

You can build a snow fort with snow. You can ski on
snow.

(a) Write a sentence that tells two other ways to have fun
with snow.

(b) Write a sentence that tells two things you **cannot** do
when there is snow on the ground.

2. **Everybody Talks About It**

What kind of weather do you like or dislike? Write a
rhyme or a paragraph to tell about it. Why do you like or
dislike that kind of weather? How does it make you feel?

Checkup
See how many List Words you can spell now.

5 The World of Work

art
earn
pancakes
strange
chief
law
job
worker
failed

nurse
painter
inspect
report
jail
collect
doctor
drive

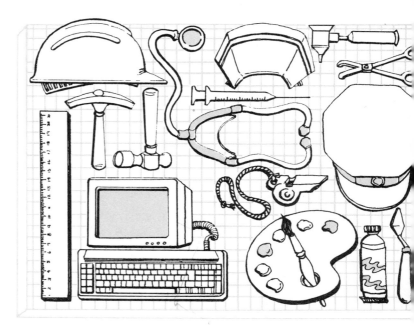

Your Class Words

Add three to five words to your list.

Checking What You Know
Underline the difficult parts of any words
you missed on the Pretest.

Meaning Connections

Help Wanted

Write the List Words that mean almost the same as the
words printed like this in the ads.

Artist needed to teach
students modern painting.
Call 555-2180.

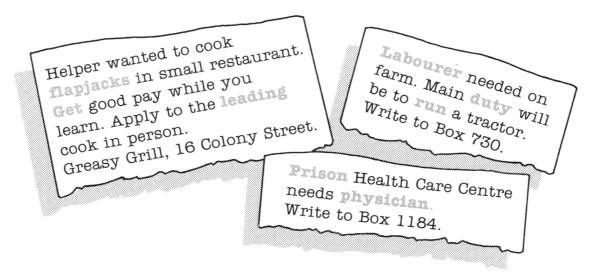

Helper wanted to cook **flapjacks** in small restaurant. **Get** good pay while you learn. Apply to the **leading** cook in person. Greasy Grill, 16 Colony Street.

Labourer needed on farm. Main **duty** will be to **run** a tractor. Write to Box 730.

Prison Health Care Centre needs **physician**. Write to Box 1184.

Pattern Connections

1. **Butcher, Baker, Candlestick Maker**

   We can add **er** to some words to make names for jobs.
   Like this:

   paint   *A painter is a person who paints.*

   (a) Add **er** to these words to make new words.

   teach   report   work   earn   drive   farm

   (b) We can make job names in other ways, too.
   Add **or** or **ist** to these words.

   collect   journal   act   inspect   novel   sail
   direct   cartoon   art   operate   type

2. **Change-a-Letter**

   You can change **job** to **sun** in three steps by changing
   one letter at a time to make new words. Here's how:

   job   **s**ob   so**n**   s**u**n

   Solve these puzzles by making new words. The arrows
   show you which letters to change.

   (a)   nurse   _ _ _ _ _   pulse

   (b)   law   _ _ _   _ _ _   mop

   (c)   art   _ _ _   _ _ _   _ _ _   his

   (d)   earn   _ _ _ _   _ _ _ _   _ _ _ _   torn

3. **The Waiter's Wages**

   (a) Many words have the **long a** sound as in cave. We spell this sound in different ways:

   (b) Add the List Words that belong in the chart.

   (c) Add two words of your own to each column.

ai	a_e
waiter	*wages*

4. **Reporter in a Scramble**

   Help! The newspaper reporter caught her notes in a sliding door. Put the word parts together to write her four key words.

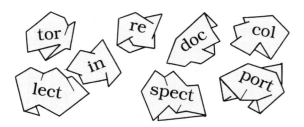

Writing Connections

1. **Where Did You Say You Work**?

   A sailor works on a ship. An acrobat works in a circus. Name seven other kinds of workers and the place where each works.

2. **What I Would Like to Do**

   Write about a job you would like to have one day. As you write, try to answer these questions:

   ● What kind of job is it?
   ● What would some of your duties be in this job?
   ● Why would you like the job?

   ▶ Exchange stories with a friend to check the spelling and the use of capital letters and punctuation marks.

> **Checkup**
> Add words you had trouble with to your Personal Spelling Dictionary.

6 Backup

painter	pumpkin	bakery	rowing	doctor
making	earn	pudding	art	lake
shaped	reporter	pushed	nobody	blow
heat	chief	standing	snowflake	September
alone	failed	stones	pancakes	clouds
wind	shine	fried	falling	tent
spread	shake	being	space	pure
stuffed	Mars	slide	warm	cold
lift-off	float	hike	job	rained
forms	October	knife	drive	water
rod	safe	nurse	sunny	cabin
thunder	there	clear	turkey	earth
sitting	fair	strange	collect	jail
country	honey	inspect	drank	during
net	life	passed	weather	hunting
path	law	camping	living	worker
rocket	God	enjoyed	taste	storm

1. Magic Squares

What words are in the squares? You can find the same word twice in each square. You can find it by reading across, and by reading down.

T	I	N
I	C	E
N	E	T

W	I	N	D
I	D	E	A
N	E	A	R
D	A	R	E

Make Magic Squares with these sets of words:

(a) cub, use, bed

(b) bat, ten, ape

(c) heat, asks, test, ease

(d) safe, area, Mars, reef

2. Word Search

In the puzzle, find 20 List Words that you could use to write about a country fair. The words go down and across. Write them in your notebook. The first word is **fair**.

```
o f a i r s l i d e c c p c n
w r a i n e d x w d d l o l q
f t n b d p u v e n j o y e d
r e p o r t r l a k e u s a c
i n u a i e i u t g f d t r f
e t m j v m n y h e s s r q s
d k p m e b g t e c e u a b n
x z k l t e b a r t g n n r t
a m i s p r e a d h k n g p z
s l n y j c o u n t r y e a l
```

3. Droodles

A weather forecaster wrote this note: SKIES
The forecaster meant: ───────
                                           CAST

Skies are overcast.

(a) Write what you think these weather droodles mean:

(1) CLOUDS   (2)   (3) S   (4)   ZERO
     ──────   C   D   N   ──────────
     HEAD   A   O   O   2 DEGREES
                      T   G   O
                      S   S   W

(b) Make up two droodles of your own. Use any words you wish.

4. Word Chains

See how long a word chain you can make. Write down a List Word. Use the last letter to start the next word. Like this:

worke**r** **r**owin**g** **G**o**d** **d**octo**r** **r**epor**t** **t**urkey

Use as many List Words as you can. Use other words too.

28

5. Odd One Out

Copy and complete the puzzle by following these four steps:

(a) In Column One, use the clues to write four-letter List Words.

(b) Use three letters from each word in Column One to write a word that fits the clue in Column Two.

(c) Write each left-out letter in the circle in the middle.

(d) Read down the circles to find a message. Numbers (1) and (11) have been done for you.

Column One		Column Two
(1) opposite of hot _cold_	©	(1) opposite of young _old_
(2) a planet; rhymes with jars	○	(2) title sometimes used with a woman's name
(3) not too hot	○	(3) uncooked
(4) trail	○	(4) a head covering
(5) opposite of death	○	(5) goblin
(6) to make money	○	(6) you hear with it
(7) door in a fence	○	(7) a hot drink
(8) water from clouds	○	(8) did run
(9) animals like mice but bigger	○	(9) drawing, painting, or sculpture
(10) not in danger	○	(10) ocean
(11) a liquid food _soup_	ⓤ	(11) soak _sop_
(12) a lot; quite a few	○	(12) month after April

Wordworks

1. **Word Web**

   (a) Susan started this word web by writing **camping** in a box. When she thought about **camping**, the words **country** and **tent** were the next words that came to her mind. What two words do you think of when you think of **tent**? And what about **country**? Copy the word web and complete it using your own words.

   (b) Now make a word web for each of these List Words:

   art, job, weather, enjoyed

2. **September Is...**

   September is back-to-school time.
   October is orange pumpkins from the garden.

   Write a September or October poem. Begin each line with September is or October is.

30

7 School Days

study   easy   teach   stories
learn   proud   idea   science
arithmetic   wall   ought   write
playground   chapter   word   reading
wrong

Your Class Words

Add three to five words your class would like to spell.

Checking What You Know

The Study Steps will help you spell any words
you missed on the Pretest.

Meaning Connections

School-day Puzzle

Use the clues to write List Words. When you are done, the
word in the pole will name a school subject.

(a) opposite of hard
(b) part of a book
(c) a thought; a plan
(d) part of a room where
      pictures go
(e) where you go at recess
(f) done with numbers
(g) you might study
      space in this subject
(h) opposite of right

(a) _ _ ☐ _
(b) _ _ _ ☐ _ _ _
(c) _ _ ☐ _
(d) _ _ _ ☐
(e) _ ☐ _ _ _ _ _ _ _
(f) _ _ ☐ _ _ _ _ _
(g) _ _ _ _ ☐ _ _
(h) _ _ _ _ ☐

Pattern Connections

1. Not Again

(a) For her class project, Donna **drew** her family tree. But she forgot one aunt, so she had to **redraw** the tree. Look up **re** in the Mini-Dictionary. Write a definition for **redraw**.

(b) Add the prefix **re** to the beginning of each of these words to write new words:

write   name   word   use   do
visit   learn   study   reading   colour

(c) Write four other words that begin with the prefix **re**.

(d) Use three of your **re** words in sentences about school.

2. School Crossing Rhymes

(a) Draw shapes like the ones below. Add letters to make crossword pairs that rhyme. (**Hint**: One word in each pair is a List Word.)

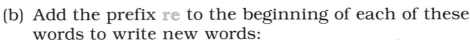

(b) Choose two other List Words and make two crossword rhymes of your own.

3. A Way with Words

(a) Donna wants to add some words to her Personal Spelling Dictionary. Help her by writing the words on each chalkboard in alphabetical order.

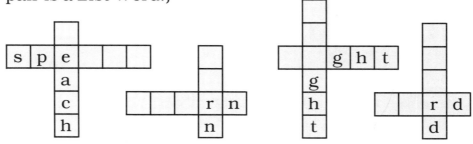

(1)
art   acting
arithmetic   alphabet

(2)
stories   should
science   study

(3)

wrong	word
won	would
write	wrote

(4)

playground	prize
player	planet
proud	painting

(b) Choose four of the words and write two sentences to tell what Donna might read about in school.

Writing Connections

1. **Your School Day**

   Donna made this chart about her school day.

Morning	Noon	Afternoon
– solve math problems – read a story	– eat lunch – play ball in playground	– study a star map in science class – write a story

   Make your own chart to show some of the things that you do in school. You may want to use List Words and Class Words in your chart.

2. **Welcome to My School**

   If a person from outer space visited your school, what three things might the creature ask you? What would your answers be? Write your imagined conversation, using quotation marks. For example:

   "Did you ever read about me in your science lessons?" asked the space creature.
   "No," I answered," we didn't even know that there were creatures like you."

   ▶ Exchange stories with a partner to check the use of quotation marks and other punctuation.

   Checkup
   See how many List Words you can spell now.

8 It's All Done with Numbers

few
both
eighteen
gather
metre
counted
litre
mass
sixty

fifteen
twelve
centimetre
less
gram
twenty
number
guess

Your Class Words
Choose three more words to add to your list.

> **Checking What You Know**
> See how many of the words you already know.

Meaning Connections

1. **Hundreds and Hundreds**

   How many cents are in a dollar? Choose and write cent
   words to fit the clues. If you need help, use a dictionary.

   (a) There are a hundred of them in a metre.   centipede
   (b) There are a hundred of them in a litre.   centilitre
   (c) a hundred years   centennial
   (d) a hundredth birthday   century
   (e) a wormlike animal with many legs   centimetre

34

2. Math Path

Use List Words to complete the sentences along the path.

(1) If you have
_____, you
have two.

(2) **Many** is
the opposite
of _____.

(3) A spoon holds
_____ than
a cup.

(5) You stand on a
scale to discover
your _____.

(4) Lou and Rosa
will win a
prize if they
_____ the
lucky number.

(6) Max _____
the candles
on the cake
to find out
how many
there were.

(7) A _____ is
less than a
kilogram.

Pattern Connections

1. Word Computer

The word computer forgot some
letters. Add **re** or **er** to complete each
incomplete word.

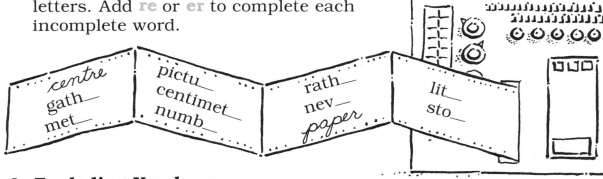

centre
gath_
met_

pictu_
centimet_
numb_

rath_
nev_
paper

lit_
sto_

2. Exploding Numbers

Watch the root word **nine** explode:

nineteenth   ninetieth = nine ≡ nineteen   ninth   ninety

Explode these root words to make as many new words as
you can.

(a) six   (b) seven   (c) eight   (d) five   (e) four

3. **Two by Two**

(a) Complete the puzzle with words that begin with the same pair of consonants.

Across

1 two times

3 sixty minus forty

Down

1 one of two born at the same time from the same mother

2 a dozen

4 comes before three

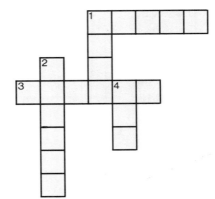

(b) List four other words that begin with the same pair of consonants as the words in the puzzle above.

(c) Use words from your list to write two sentences.

Writing Connections

1. **The No-Frown Clown**

   The no-frown clown was two metres tall.
   The no-frown clown had twelve balloons on strings.
   Use List Words to write four more sentences about a no-frown clown.

2. **Party Plans**

   Pretend your class is going to have a party. Write a paragraph to tell all the things you must do to get ready. Why are you having the party? When will it be? How many invitations will you need to send out? What types of food will you serve? What games will you play?

   ▶ Exchange paragraphs with a partner to check the spelling and punctuation.

   Checkup
   How many List Words can you spell now?

⑨ What's Inside?

boxes   camel   trunk
plenty   bottle   bookcase
remain   filled   couple
baskets   tank   money
candle   barrel   look
mice   apples

Your Class Words
Choose three more words to add to your list.

Checking What You Know
How many of the words can you already spell?

Meaning Connections

The Magic Basement

Complete the story by writing the List Words that mean almost the same as the words printed like this .

Our basement is a magical place packed with lots of interesting things.

In one corner are old books on a shelf. I like to glance at them on rainy days. Beside the books is an empty fish aquarium that has a pair of shells in it.

There is a glass jug that sits on top of a metal chest under the stairs. The chest is empty but the jug has a half-melted wax light inside it!

Do you have a magical place filled with old treasures?

37

Pattern Connections

1. **A Little Mix-up**

   (a) When the basement was cleaned the List Words in the box lost their double consonants and got all mixed up. Add the double letters and unscramble each List Word. For example: **ille** = *little*

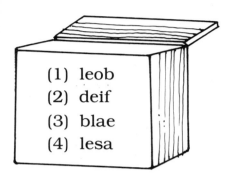

   (1) leob
   (2) deif
   (3) blae
   (4) lesa

   (b) Write five other words that have double consonants.

2. **Plenty of Things**

   Change each word printed like this so that it can be used in the sentence. Rewrite the sentences.

   (a) fill, box   The movers _____ their truck with all kinds of different _____.

   (b) remain, remain   There were only three days _____ in the month, so when his family went on a trip, Tim _____ behind.

   (c) look, mouse   When I opened the old trunk and _____ inside, I was surprised to see three _____.

   (d) bottle, bottle   Aunt Ruth was working in a _____ plant. Each day she _____ hundreds of cases of fruit juice.

3. **A Box of Word Pieces**

   (a) Each jigsaw-puzzle piece is part of a List Word. Put the parts together to write the six List Words.

   (b) Choose four of the words you just wrote and use them in two sentences.

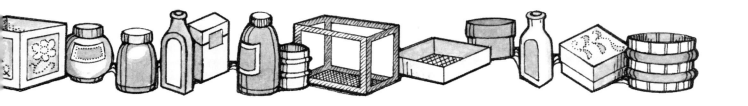

4. A Barrel Full of Pickles

(a) Write the words **little** and **pickle**. Say each word to yourself and notice the sound of the **le** ending.

(b) Now write the words **jewel** and **gravel** and say each to yourself. How does the sound of the **el** ending compare with the sound of the **le** ending in part (**a**)?

(c) Add the List Words and three others to complete the chart.

litt**le**	jew**el**
pickle	*gravel*

(d) Use two of the words in a riddle. For example:

What happened to the little cucumber in the jar? It got into a pickle.

Writing Connections

1. A B C of What's Inside

For each of the first five letters of the alphabet, make a list of as many things as you can think of that might be found inside the Magic Basement. You might wish to start your lists like this:

A — *apples* ...
B — *barrel* ...
C — *camel* ...
D —?
E —?

2. What's That? A Secret Door?

What would you do in the Magic Basement? What might you hear, touch, see, and smell there? Write a story or a poem about it.

▶ Reread your story or poem to see if you need to add describing words to make it more interesting.

Checkup

Add any words you had trouble with to your Personal Spelling Dictionary.

---

10 Oh, What a Feeling!

feelings   delight   somebody
smiled   excite   anybody
happier   needed   interesting
proudly   scared   angry
fear   joyful   sorry
pleased   tear

Your Class Words
Choose three more emotion words to add
to your list.

> ### Checking What You Know
> The chart on your Pretest will help you
> to see why you made any errors.

Meaning Connections

1. **Who's That Smiling Back at Me**

   Complete each sentence by writing the List Word that
   means almost the same as the word printed like this.

   (a) I **grinned** at Sally, and she _____ back at me.

   (b) Avtar is **furious**, but he won't be _____ for long.

   (c) I'm _____ to hear that you are feeling **unhappy**

   (d) Rosa will be **glad** to sing such a _____ song.

   (e) Mark needed **someone** to help him, so I hope _____
   was there.

   (f) Erin used **fascinating** words to write an _____ story.

40

2. **A Happy Chain**

   (a) Continue each word chain by writing as many words as you can that are **synonyms**. You will find some of the words in your Mini-Thesaurus.

   (1) h a p p y   *cheerful*   ?   ?
   (2) s c a r e d   ?   ?   ?
   (3) d e l i g h t   ?   ?   ?

   (b) Write a List Word that is an **antonym** of each of these words. For example:

   sorrowful – joyful

   (1) displeased   (3) sadder   (5) courage
   (2) humbly   (4) nobody   (6) calm

3. **A Couple of Tears**

   In your Mini-Dictionary you will find two listings for tear.

   (a) Write the meaning of tear when it rhymes with fear.

   (b) Write the meaning of tear when it rhymes with pear.

   (c) Write sentences to show the two meanings of tear.

Pattern Connections

1. **Full of Joy**

   This chart shows two meanings of the suffix ful:

"full of; showing"	"enough to fill"
cheerful	*cupful*

   (a) Copy the chart in your notebook. Add ful to each word and write the new word under the correct heading.

   spoon   delight   mouth   wonder   peace   tear
   joy   use   power   fear   hand   room

   (b) Use ful words from both columns of your chart in two sentences or verses about feelings. For example:

   A cupful of orange juice starts my day in a cheerful way.

2. Happy, Happier, Happiest

Jeff feels happy. Marie feels happier.
Lee feels the happiest.

Copy and complete this chart:

y	*happy*			*scary*	*needy*
er		*angrier*			
est			*sorriest*		

3. Mixed-up Emotions

(a) Unscramble the List Word and rewrite the sentence:
Did you hurt his glfeneis?

(b) See how many words you can make from the letters in the List Word you just wrote.

Writing Connections

1. Colour Me Curious

(a) Write the feeling words below. Beside each, write the colour that you think fits best.

happiness   loneliness   excitement   fear

(b) For each colour you used write a sentence to tell why it fits the feeling. For example:

When people are angry, they feel hot and their faces turn red like fire.

2. How Do You Feel?

What makes you happy...angry...sad? Write two paragraphs about some of the feelings you have had.

▶ Exchange paragraphs with a partner to check the spelling and punctuation.

> **Checkup**
> See how many List Words you can spell now.

11 From Many Lands

build   among
fort   brave
plain   cheered
beaver   furs
built   lead
French   secret
knowing animals
spoke   meat
shoot

Your Class Words
Add five words your class would like to spell.

Checking What You Know
See how many of the words you already know.

Meaning Connections

Early Days

Helga is making jot-notes for a report on the early days of her town. Write List Words to complete her notes.

–town began as a __1__ with a high wooden fence around it.
–traders got glossy beaver __2__ from Native Peoples.
–traders ate __3__ from deer and other wild __4__ .
–soon settlers came to farm on the flat __5__ near the fort.
–settlers __6__ many languages, such as English, __7__ ,
 and German.

Pattern Connections

1. **Settlers' Trail**

   Write the past forms of the action words to help
   the settlers find their trail. (**Hint**: These past forms do not
   use **ed**.)

Present time	Past time
build	— — — — —
lead	— — —
know	— — — —
shoot	— — — —
speak	— — — — —

   The letters along the trail should spell the
   name of something some settlers slept in.

2. **The Secret Place**

   (a) Many words have the **long e** sound as in **speak**
   We spell this sound in several different ways:

e	ea	ee
equal	*meaning*	*freedom*

   In the following story, find six more words with the
   long e sound. Write them under the correct spelling
   patterns in the chart.

   Even though the settlers' children had a hard life,
   they still had time for fun. One day they were in their
   secret hiding place by the pond. They watched a
   mother beaver lead her little ones across the water.
   Seeing the beavers play made the children feel happy.

   (b) Add two more words to each column in the chart.

44

3. **Anagrams**

Use all of the letters in each of the following words to write a List Word. Like this:

shore — horse

(a) team   (b) pokes   (c) deal   (d) hoots   (e) mango

4. **Plains of Grain**

(a) Write the List Word that rhymes with each of these:

(1) short   (2) folk   (3) growing   (4) save   (5) trench

(b) Choose three of the words you just wrote and use them in two sentences about the early Canadian settlers.

Writing Connections

1. **Canadian Animals**

The moose and the bear are wild animals that live in Canada. Name six more wild Canadian animals.

2. **Run Like a Deer**

(a) We sometimes compare people to animals. For example:

hungry as a wolf   sing like a bird

Write five more ways we could compare people to animals.

(b) Choose four of your comparisons and use them in sentences.

> **Checkup**
> Write in your Personal Spelling Dictionary any words you had trouble with.

study	proudly	delight	among	litre
few	beaver	wall	joyful	science
build	candle	excite	apples	gram
feelings	wrong	twelve	metre	write
boxes	counted	spoke	ought	fort
learn	meat	filled	somebody	lead
smiled	fear	tank	brave	twenty
both	bottle	chapter	centimetre	money
interesting	easy	needed	remain	secret
baskets	pleased	sixty	trunk	angry
arithmetic	less	shoot	word	reading
happier	built	plenty	anybody	French
plain	camel	teach	cheered	look
eighteen	proud	scared	mice	animals
bookcase	couple	fifteen	stories	sorry
playground	knowing	barrel	tear	number
gather	mass	idea	furs	guess

1. **Hide and Seek**

   (a) Find and write the eight List Words hiding in the sentences. For example:

   D**id** **ea**ch unc**le ad**d one picture?—*idea, lead*

   (1) Everyone who came late, please meet me at the corner.

   (2) Skiers glide lightly past me treasuring the happy moments.

   (3) The noisy owls hooted at the slow alligator.

   (4) Bess cared for the sick bird.

(b) Choose a List Word and hide it in your own sentence. See if a friend can find your hiding List Word.

2. Crossword Days

Write the List Words that complete the puzzle:

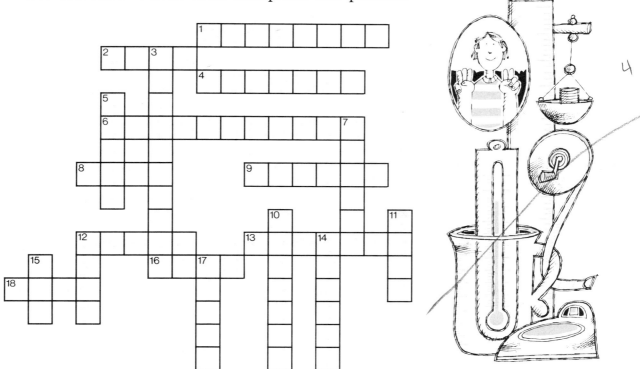

Across

1 a case for books
2 more than one mouse
4 the study of nature; first part rhymes with pie
6 not dull or boring
8 a unit to measure mass
9 total number of fingers and toes most people have
12 a unit to measure length
13 shouted praise; rhymes with feared
16 not difficult
18 opposite of more

Down

3 there are a hundred in a metre
5 a unit to measure volume of liquids such as milk
7 to collect; bring together
10 a part of a book
11 a thought
12 you use a scale to measure this
14 to stir up feelings; last part rhymes with kite
15 not many
17 said something

3. Change-a-Letter

You can often change one letter in a word to make a new word. For example:

me**a**t   melt   wor**d**   work   **n**oon   loon

Find five List Words that you can do this with. Write the new words you make.

4. Word Stairs

See how long you can keep the stairs going. Use the last letter of a List Word to start a new List Word.

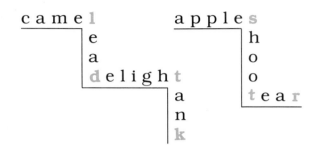

5. Parts Puzzle

(a) Help! The word parts are all mixed up. Unscramble them to write ten List Words with l in them.

tle   bar   ings   ples   ly   feel   an   ful   i   mals   de
ap   tre   rel   light   can   joy   bot   dle   li   proud

(b) Write your ten l words in alphabetical order.

6. Fox and Dogs Code

(a) A secret code can be based on a sentence, like this:

T	H	E	Q	U	I	C	K	B	R	O	W	N	F	O	X	J	U	M	P	S
A	B	C	D	E	F	G	H	I	J	K	L	M	N	*	O	P	*	Q	R	S

O	V	E	R	L	A	Z	Y	D	O	G	S	.
*	T	*	*	U	V	W	X	Y	*	Z	*	

(b) Use the Fox and Dogs code to decode these messages:

(1) S U E P U V   Q X X P
    H U K B F Q   Z T W W.

(2) N U U V   N U   B F   J W T D C P X L F Q.

(c) Write a message of your own in the Fox and Dogs code.

48

Wordworks

1. **Alphabet Poem**

   C raving food
   D islike feeling
   E mpty stomach
   F ainting feeling
   Oooh! peanut-butter cookies! Yum

   The first four lines of the alphabet poem begin with words in alphabetical order. The last line begins with any letter and sums up the poem. Pick four letters and write an alphabet poem using one of these ideas:

   feelings, animals, science, boxes

2. **As Hungry as a Wolf**

   We can use **like** or **as** to compare things. For example:

   The snow covered the ground like a blanket.
   Maria was as hungry as a wolf.

   We can also make comparisons **without** using **like** or **as**.
   For example:

   A blanket of snow covered the ground.
   Maria wolfed down her lunch.

   (a) Write a sentence using **like** or **as** to compare

(1) children to ghosts.	(4) a baby's cheeks to apples.
(2) flames to tongues.	(5) students to beavers.
(3) tears to rain.	(6) a bicycle to an airplane.

   (b) Choose two of your comparisons and rewrite each in a sentence **without** using **like** or **as**.

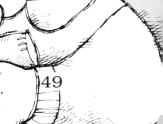

49

13 In Style

wearing   belt
zipper   pocket
change   glasses
tidy   smartly
cords   comb
instead   jewels
woolen   clothes
dressed   shoes
scarf

Your Class Words

Add three more words to your list.

Checking What You Know

The Study Steps will help you spell any words
you missed on the Pretest.

Meaning Connections

1. **Clues Closet**

   Write one List Word for each pair of clues:

   (a) they're bright and shiny; synonym for gems

   (b) another name for corduroy pants;
   used to plug lamps into wall sockets

   (c) you wear it around your neck;
   last three letters spell a sound a dog makes

2. **Matching Word Pairs**

Write the List Words that complete these pairs:

(a) Gloves are to hands as _____ are to feet.

(b) Money is to purse as wallet is to _____.

(c) Wooden is to trees as _____ is to sheep.

(d) Crutches are to walking as _____ are to seeing.

(e) Books are to carrying as clothes are to _____.

(f) Tie is to neck as _____ is to waist.

Pattern Connections

1. **Dresser Drawer**

(a) Choose a consonant pair from the dresser drawer to complete each pair of words.

(1) __ean __othes
(2) __arlet __arf
(3) __ably __essed
(4) __ittering __oves
(5) __inny __irts
(6) __ockings in__ead
(7) __iling __artly

Dresser drawer containing consonant pairs: gl, tr, sc, cl, dr, sm, st, br, sk

(b) Choose three of the consonant pairs and write one word pair of your own for each.

2. **Exploding Words**

Watch the root word suit explode:

suited   suitably   unsuitable   suits
unsuitably   suiting   suit   unsuited   suitable

Explode these root words. Write as many new words as you can. Use a dictionary to make sure each new word makes sense.

(a) comb   (b) change

51

3. **Opposites with un**

The prefix **un** often means "not." We add **un** to some words to make them mean the opposite. For example:

tied—**un**tied   real—**un**real

Rewrite the following description. Change each word printed like this to its opposite.

   The Frog Prince's vest looked tidy. His pockets were zipped. His horse's long mane was combed and dressed. Zap! went the fairy godmother's wand.

   "I'm unchanged!" the Frog Prince exclaimed.

4. **Pattern T-shirts**

Draw the following T-shirts. Make each T-shirt longer by adding four more words with the same spelling pattern.

Writing Connections

1. **Zip and Tie**

Jackets often have zippers. Write sentences about three other things with zippers.

2. **Change Your Clothes**

We wear different clothes at different times. Choose seasons, sports, or holidays and write sentences to describe the clothes you wear for them.

> **Checkup**
> How many of the List Words can you spell now?

14 Family Ties

special   aunt
picnic   uncle
visiting   raise
loving   since
fond   forgot
parents   unless
cousin   move
others   family
married

Your Class Words
Add three to five more words.

> **Checking What You Know**
> The chart on your Pretest will help you to see why you made any errors.

Meaning Connections

1. A Family Memory

Write the List Words that complete this story:

Last September Mom and Dad and I were __1__ my aunt and uncle and my cousin Billy on their farm. My little __2__ Billy and I were having so much fun riding Billy's pony that we __3__ all about lunch. But my aunt

continued on the next page...   53

and __4__ had a __5__ treat waiting for us. __6__ it was such a beautiful day, we had a family __7__ outdoors beside the garden. It was a great way to end the summer holidays.

2. **Speaking of Relatives...**

   Write the List Words that fit these meaning clues:

   (a) having a husband or wife

   (b) liking; rhymes with **pond**

   (c) mothers and fathers

   (d) your mother's or father's sister

   (e) a child of your parent's brother or sister

Pattern Connections

1. **How Do You Say That?**

   (a) Look up the word **others** in the Mini-Dictionary. The coded word that comes after **others** tells you how to say the word. The **Sound Key** at the beginning of the dictionary tells how to use the code.

   (b) Here are the sound codes for some of the List Words. Break the code and write each List Word.

(1) (rāz)	(4) (un les′)	(7) (fər got′)
(2) (kuz′ ən)	(5) (spesh′ əl)	(8) (viz′ it ing)
(3) (mūv)	(6) (fam′ə lē)	(9) (luv′ ing)

2. **Word Parts**

   A word's sound code also tells you how many parts the word has. The word **cousin** has two parts. Write the number of parts that are in each of the words in **1.(b)**.

3. **A Little Stress**

   Say the word **picnic**. Notice that you stress the first word part. Now look at the sound code for **picnic**: (pik′ nik). The **stress mark** (′) tells you that the first part (pik′) is stressed.

54

(a) Look back at the sound codes in **1.(b)**. For the two-part words, list the words with their first part stressed.

(b) List the words with their second part stressed.

(c) Add three other two-part words to each of your lists. To help you decide where the stress goes, say each word to yourself.

Writing Connections

1. **Acrostic Poems**

   D eep blue eyes
   a lways kind
   n ephew who is special to me.

   Use the letters in a family member's name to write your own acrostic poem.

2. **Image Poems**

   An image is a picture you have in your mind.

   Whispy white hair and quick lively footsteps
   Darting eyes watching every
   Bird and squirrel and butterfly—
   Grandpa walking with his big brown hound.

   Think of a person who is special to you. What images come to your mind? Write a poem to describe these images. Tell who you are describing at the end of your poem.

   > **Checkup**
   > Always add any words you need to study to your Personal Spelling Dictionary.

15 Special Days

August   November   shiny
June   December   surprised
July   March   April
May   February   giant
sent   January   birthday
invite   month

Your Class Words
Add three to five more words to your list.

> **Checking What You Know**
> Use the Study Steps to help you spell any words you missed.

Meaning Connections

Month Riddles

Use List Words to answer these month riddles:

(1) I'm a month of gift-giving and have the year's shortest day.
(2) I have fewer days than all the other months.
(3) I'm the month of "Happy Birthday, Canada."
(4) I'm the month of "School's Out" and the year's longest day.
(5) I'm the month of the fool of the first.
(6) I'm named after the Roman ruler Augustus.
(7) I lead all the rest.

Pattern Connections

1. **Birthday List**

   (a) Marco and Sylvia are making a list of their classmates' birthdays:

   Jasmine—June 8
   Carl—May 23

   There are nine short forms of the names of the months in the puzzle. Find and write them to help Marco and Sylvia finish their list.

D	S	C.	L	O	R	S	A
E	E	H	N	F	B	T	Q.
A	P	R.	D	E	C.	R	T
U	T.	J	K.	B.	N	I	V
G.	M	A	R.	J	O	C	T.
F	G.	N.	I	M.	V.	C	P

   (b) Make your own birthday list. Put four of your friends or family members on your list.

2. **Does It Fit?**

   Look carefully at the letter patterns. Write the word that does not fit. The first one is done for you.

   (a) September, October, November, December—*October*
   (b) March, February, January, May
   (c) both, moth, month, brother
   (d) centimetre, centre, sent, recent
   (e) friendly, birthday, slowly, early

3. **I Spy**

(a) Many words have the **long i** sound as in **time**. We spell this sound in several different ways:

Add the List Words with the **long i** sound to the chart.

i	i_e	y
child	alive	reply
lion	beside	myself

(b) Add three words of your own to each column.

(c) Use words from your chart to write two sentences about birthdays.

Writing Connections

1. **A Month of Surprises**

Use your own ideas to complete each sentence starter:

(a) In December I would be surprised if...

(b) March would be a nicer month if...because...

2. **Thank You, Aunt Mabel**

November 28, 19__

Dear Aunt Mabel,

Thank you for the toboggan you sent for my birthday. My friend Ralph and I have lots of fun with it.

Grandpa Burns came over for my birthday. We had chocolate cake with white candles.

Mom wants to know if you can visit us on New Year's Day. I hope you will.

Your loving nephew,
Gerry

Write a letter thanking someone for doing something special for you. Check your spelling and punctuation.

> **Checkup**
> Always add any words you need to study to your Personal Spelling Dictionary.

16 Anybody Home?

side   cupboard
broad   closet
bath   roof
size   steps
bigger   upstairs
wide   nail
stairs   floor
bedroom   high
kitchen

Your Class Words

Add more words your class would like to spell.

Checking What You Know

See how many of the words you already know.

Meaning Connections

Household Words

Write the headings down the left-hand side of your notebook page. Write the List Words beside the headings where they belong. Some words can go beside more than one heading.

(a) Names of rooms

(b) Other house parts

(c) Words to describe houses

(d) Places to store things

(e) Other words

Pattern Connections

1. **Creaky, Creakier, Creakiest**

   Add either **er** or **est** to each word to complete the word pole. The word in the pole will answer this riddle:

   What do creaky door hinges need?

   (a) big   **er**
   (b) wide   **er**
   (c) high   **est**
   (d) broad **est**
   (e) skinny **est**
   (f) thin   **er**

   (a) _ _ _ ☐ _ _
   (b) _ _ _ _ ☐
   (c) _ _ _ _ ☐ _ _
   (d) _ _ _ ☐ _ _ _ _
   (e) _ _ _ _ _ _ _ ☐ _
   (f) _ _ _ _ _ ☐ _

2. **Guiding Words**

   In your Mini-Dictionary, the word at the top of the left-hand column of each page tells you the first word you will find on that page. The word at the top of the right-hand column tells you the last word you will find. These words are called **guide words**.

   Write the two guide words at the top of the page in your Mini-Dictionary where each of these List Words is found.

   (a) broad   (c) kitchen   (e) size
   (b) upstairs   (d) floor   (f) closet

3. **The Right Part**

   Here is an easy way to find a word in your dictionary. Imagine that your dictionary is divided into these three equal parts:

   (1) [a-h]   (2) [i-p]   (3) [q-z]

   (a) Write the List Words that you would find in the **a-h** part.

   (b) Write the List Words that you would find in **q-z**.

   (c) Write the List Words that you would find in the middle part.

60

4. Patterns in Sentences

Complete the sentences with words having the following spelling patterns. The first one is done for you.

ai   (a)   I hammered in a *nail* but it *failed* to hold the wood.

airs   (b)   We sat on _____ near the _____.

ide   (c)   The chimney is twenty centimetres _____ on each _____.

oo   (d)   We have a _____ over our heads and a _____ under our feet.

igh   (e)   That cupboard _____ be too _____ for you to reach.

ath   (f)   After finishing her _____ homework, she took a _____.

Writing Connections

1. Home Sweet Home

Some people live in houses. Some live in palaces. Name four other types of homes.

2. Dream House

Choose a type of home that you would like to live in. Write a paragraph telling why you would like to live there.

> **Checkup**
> How many of the List Words can you spell now?

17 It's Hockey Time

strong   period
greatest   coach
faster   pass
minutes   hockey
quickly   goalie
scored   face-off
centre   quit
able   player
skated

Your Class Words
Add up to five more words.

Checking What You Know
The Study Steps will help you to spell any words you missed on the Pretest.

Meaning Connections

1. **Hawks and Rockets**

Use List Words to help Jean finish her report.

Friday the Hawks and Rockets played their best game so far this h__1__ season. Two m__2__ into the first p__3__, Mary Corbini of the Hawks won a f__4__ at centre ice. She s__5__ down the ice to p__6__ the puck to

Alan Peck. Skating q 7 , Peck outdistanced the Rocket p 8 who tried to catch him. With a s 9 wrist shot, he was a 10 to beat g 11 Guy Bond. The Hawks s 12 two other goals in the game, winning 3-0.

2. **Hockey Synonyms**

Find the List Words that mean the same as the words printed like this and rewrite these sentences:

Hockey is one of the best sports in the world. Each player is a powerful athlete. Some players can deliver the puck better than others, and some are speedier skaters. But even the goaltender must be able to skate swiftly. The trainer makes sure that each athlete stays fit.

Pattern Connections

1. **Compounds with Hyphens**

(a) **The quick-tempered player was angry about losing the face-off.**

Which words in the sentence were made by joining two words? In some compounds we join the words with a short line called a **hyphen**.

Use the following words to write five compounds with hyphens.

(b) Check in a dictionary to make sure all your words are compounds.

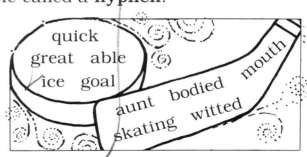

quick
great able
ice goal
aunt bodied mouth
skating witted

2. **A Hockey Mix-up**

(a) Unscramble the List Words in this sentence and write the sentence.

The puck was dropped at trceen ice to start the first ipredo.

(b) See how many words you can make from the letters in each of the List Words you just wrote.

3. **Quick! Score a Goal!**

   (a) Solve the puzzle. Each answer begins with the same two letters.

   Across

   6 not loud

   7 25 cents

   Down

   1 stop

   2 an argument

   3 rapidly

   4 a prince's mother

   5 what a duck says

   (b) Write four other words that begin with those two letters. Look in your Personal Spelling Dictionary.

Writing Connections

1. **Name That Team**

   Make up three new names for hockey teams.

2. **Cheering Keeps You Warm**

   Hurrah for the Rockets,
   Stamp on the floor,
   Stand up,
   Sit down,
   Score, score, score!

   Make up two more five-line hockey cheers of your own. You may wish to use some of the following words to start:

   Go team, go...

   Our team is the best...

   > **Checkup**
   > Record in your Personal Spelling Dictionary any words you missed.

Backup

strong	period	uncle	comb	cousin
side	special	visiting	invite	forgot
August	greatest	instead	loving	coach
wearing	zipper	glasses	goalie	scored
May	smartly	fond	nail	March
broad	stairs	kitchen	woolen	change
January	high	hockey	floor	cords
bath	face-off	roof	centre	unless
month	aunt	February	parents	others
size	tidy	pocket	November	player
shiny	June	birthday	able	clothes
bigger	picnic	sent	jewels	married
surprised	faster	upstairs	skated	scarf
wide	pass	minutes	December	move
cupboard	April	steps	dressed	shoes
belt	July	raise	quit	family
closet	bedroom	quickly	since	giant

1. **Headlines Hide List Words**

   Find and write the List Word hiding in
   each newspaper headline. For example:

   Del**hi gh**ost seen again—*high*

   (a) Grandpa rents old cottage

   (b) Recent report made public

   (c) Children have fun cleaning up city park

   (d) Last air show for pilot

   (e) Mayor's car fails to start

2. **Drop-a-Letter**

Drop a letter from each word printed **like this** to write a word that completes the sentence. The first one is done for you.

(a) I **tried** to undo the knot she _tied_.

(b) A **snail** crawled over the rusty _____.

(c) It will be **sunless** today _____ the clouds go away.

(d) The swings are on the left _____ of the **slide**.

(e) Are you _____ to set the **table**?

(f) The **closet** was _____ to the bedroom window.

(g) Pat _____ two eggs for her **friend**.

(h) They _____ trying to mend the **quilt**.

3. **Word Search**

Find and write 14 List Words you could use to write about clocks and calendars. Some words go around to the right. Some go towards the centre. The first word is **August**.

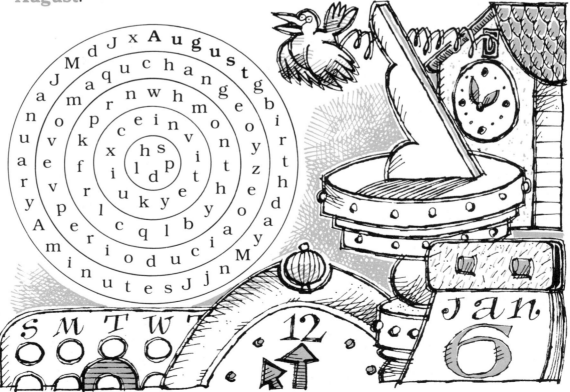

4. Happy New Year Code

Helen's grandpa can speak Arabic, Icelandic, and Portuguese. This is how you say "Happy New Year" in each language:

KULLA BIKAIR (Arabic)

GLEDILEGT NYAR (Icelandic)

FELIZ ANO NOVO (Portuguese)

(a) Helen's grandpa wrote her a note using this code:

(b) Use the Happy New Year Code to decode the note Helen received:

K	U	L	L	A	B	I	K	A	I	R
A	B	C	D	E	F	G	H	I	J	K

G	L	E	D	I	L	E	G	T	N	Y	A	R
L	*	M	N	*	*	O	P	Q	R	S	*	T

F	E	L	I	Z	A	N	O	N	O	V	O
U	*	V	*	W	*	*	Y	*	*	Z	*

LEEA RE EO
YGALAKG
KEGALKO GKNRO
IKDFKNO BANYR.

(c) Write a message of your own in the Happy New Year code.

5. Double Bubbles

(a) Find the four List Words with double o.

(b) Write them in the o-bubble in alphabetical order. The letters in boxes should spell something you have above your eye.

(c) Find the four List Words with double s.

(d) Write them in the s-bubble in alphabetical order. The letters in boxes should spell a synonym for true.

Wordworks

1. **Clothes to You**

Benny, a hockey-playing mouse, is getting ready for a game with his friends...

> Benny pulled on red plastic skates with gold safety pin blades. Then came his shining silver helmet made from the tip of a cigar case. The three mice wore matching red, blue, and white sweaters.

—from *Mice at Centre Ice* by Estelle Salata

Think of a story you have read. What did the people or animals wear? Write three sentences to tell about their clothes.

2. **What Will the Bear Wear?**

Think of some people or animals that you could write a story about. What will they wear? Write jot-notes to describe their clothes. Then write a story about what they do.

19 What a Place for an Adventure!

waited   closer   boil
hiding   beside   remained
middle   hopped   foggy
stopped   bushes   running
between   above   across
deep   follow

Your Class Words

Add three words to your list.

> **Checking What You Know**
> Underline the hard parts of any words you
> missed on the Pretest.

Meaning Connections

1. **Lost in the Forest**

   Write the List Words that complete this story:

   One damp __1__ night a farm pig and a rooster were
   lost in the forest. At last they saw a hut __2__ a tall fir
   tree. They crept over to the window, __3__ themselves
   behind a tall clump of __4__ . The pig tried to look inside,
   but the window was too far __5__ her head.

   So the rooster __6__ up onto the pig's head and peered
   through the window. Inside he saw a man starting
   to __7__ a chicken in a big pot. "Squawk! Let's get out of
   here!" shrieked the rooster. The two friends
   started __8__ as fast as they could, back into the forest.

2. **This Way to Adventure**

(a) Match **Part A** words with **Part B** words to write word groups that go together. You may use **Part B** words more than once. For example:

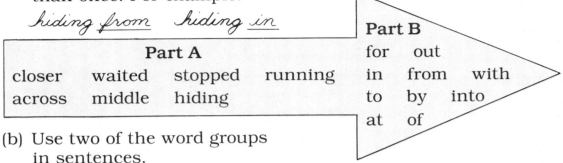

hiding from   hiding in

Part A				Part B		
closer	waited	stopped	running	in	from	with
across	middle	hiding		to	by	into
				at	of	

(for   out)

(b) Use two of the word groups in sentences.

Pattern Connections

1. **A Way with Words**

(a) Lucy's uncle sailed away on an adventure. He brought home treasure chests for Lucy. Help Lucy unlock each chest by writing the words in alphabetical order.

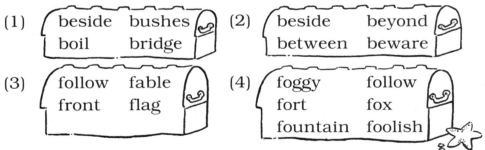

(1) beside   bushes
     boil   bridge

(2) beside   beyond
     between   beware

(3) follow   fable
     front   flag

(4) foggy   follow
     fort   fox
     fountain   foolish

(b) Use four of the words in sentences about an adventure you would like to have.

2. **In the Middle of a Muddle**

(a) Many words have double letters. Write the List Words that fit in the following chart:

dd	ee	gg	ll	nn	pp	ss
saddle	*jeep*	*baggage*	*cellar*	*funny*	*snappy*	*hissing*

(b) Add two more words to each list in the chart. You may find some in your Personal Spelling Dictionary.

3. Quick-Change Artist

Change List Words to fit the clues. All the words you write should end in **er**. The first one is done for you. When you are finished, the word in the pole will name a player on a baseball team.

(a) I come behind.

(b) I serve people in a restaurant.

(c) I am an insect that hops in the grass.

(d) I am a tank to heat water in.

(e) I am what is left over when you divide.

(f) I plug up the top of a bottle.

(g) I move quickly in a race.

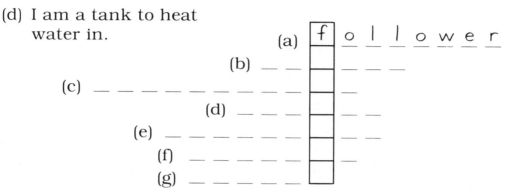

Writing Connections

1. Where in the World?

An adventure could take place deep in a mine, across the ocean, or above the clouds. Name three more places where people or animals could have an adventure.

2. All Aboard for Adventure

What could happen in an adventure? It could include a chase, a battle, a rescue, or a journey. Write a story about people or animals having an adventure.

▶ Reread your story to see if you need to add more action words and describing words to make it more exciting.

> **Checkup**
> How many of the words can you spell now?

20 Popcorn Time

answer   ponies
tonight   master
police   peaches
sound   cherry
movie   monster
ticket   popcorn
dead   ghost
ranch   castle
chase

Your Class Words
Add three to five words.

Checking What You Know
See how many of the words you already know.

Meaning Connections

Movie Review

Write the List Words that mean almost the same as the words
printed like this.

    "Little Heroes" is the kind of motion picture I like. It's
about two children living on a farm who spoil the plans of
an evil monster that wants to become ruler of the world.
    Riding small horses, the two heroes go after the
monster to a dark cave. Bravely, the children enter the

cave. What happens next? I won't reply to that question because I hope you see "Little Heroes" yourself. It's playing this evening at the Nova Theatre. Don't forget to buy some fluffy white kernels to munch on.

Pattern Connections

1. **Change Chart**

   Write the List Word that fits the meaning clue on the left. Then make letter changes in the List Word and write the new word that fits the meaning clue on the right. The first row is done for you.

(a)	large farm	*ranch*	*branch*	part of a tree
(b)	noise	?	?	kind of dog
(c)	not living	?	?	part of a sandwich
(d)	bus fare	?	?	kind of bug
(e)	palace	?	?	cows
(f)	law officers	?	?	having good manners

2. **How to Say It**

   (a) Help the movie actor say her words correctly. Here are the sound codes for some of the List Words. Break the code and write each List Word. The first one is done for you.

   (1) (pə lēs') *police*   (4) (kas' əl) _____

   (2) (chās) _____   (5) (an' sər) _____

   (3) (mon' stər) _____   (6) (gōst) _____

   (b) Did you notice the three words with silent consonants? Copy the chart and add each word where it belongs:

Silent h	Silent t	Silent w
honest	*fasten*	*write*
rhyme	*thistle*	*wrinkle*

73

3. **Making Movies**

   (a) The movie director needs five of each of these things. Copy and complete the chart by making each word mean **more than one**.

monster	witch
ranch	cherry
pony	castle
ghost	peach

Just add s.	Add es.	Change y to i —Add es.

   (b) Add two more words to each movie screen.

   (c) Use four of the words in sentences about movies.

Writing Connections

1. **At the Movies**

   Complete this word web. Say **movies** to yourself and write two words it makes you think of. Now write two words for each of the two words you just wrote.

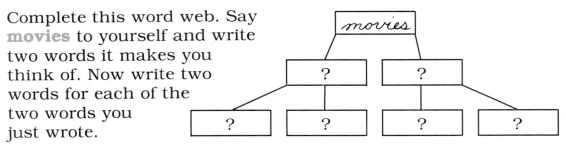

2. **You the Reviewer**

   Write a short review of a movie or TV show that you liked. Try to answer all of these questions:

   (a) What is the name of the movie or TV show?

   (b) Who are some of the characters in it?

   (c) Where does the action take place?

   (d) What happens?

   (e) Why do you like the movie or TV show?

   Checkup
   See how many List Words you can spell now.

74

21 Buyers and Sellers

seller   coin   sign
owner   sold   become
closed   belong   pear
whole   paid   cent
bought   saved   spend
silver   chance

Your Class Words

Choose three more words to add to your list.

> **Checking What You Know**
> Use the Study Steps every day to learn new words.

Meaning Connections

1. **Sail for Sale**

   Some pairs of words sound the same but have different spellings and meanings. For example:

   buy and by

   (a) Complete each sentence by writing a List Word that sounds the same as one word in the sentence.

       (1) Why did the ticket _____ go down into the cellar?

       (2) If we had one more _____, we could have sent it.

       (3) In the _____ drawer there was only one sock without a hole in it.

       (4) A pair of girls bought four apples and a _____.

   (b) Use two of the word pairs in sentences.

2. Shopping Spree

Use the clues to write List Words. When you are finished, the word in the pole should tell you where you can do your shopping.

(a) opposite of bought

(b) another name for a penny

(c) to grow to be

(d) what metal coins are made of

(e) someone who sells

(f) opposite of opened

(a) ☐ _ _ _

(b) _ _ _ ☐

(c) _ _ _ ☐ _

(d) _ _ _ _ ☐ _

(e) _ _ _ _ ☐ _

(f) _ _ _ ☐ _ _

Pattern Connections

1. Sign Here Please

(a) This sign can be a wink or a wave: *signal*
   Write the sign word that

   (1) is a drawing or a plan.

   (2) is to give up a job.

   (3) is a person's name written by that person.

   (4) is a thing used to point out something.

(b) Use two of your sign words in a sentence.

2. Lost Car

Help the shoppers find their lost car in the parking lot. Write the past forms of the action words. The letters along the trail should spell the colour of the car. (**Hint:** Some past forms do not use ed.)

Present time	Past time
pay	_ _ _ _
save	_ _ _ _ _
sell	_ _ _ _
spend	_ _ _ _ _
become	_ _ _ _ _ _
belong	_ _ _ _ _ _ _
buy	_ _ _ _ _ _
own	_ _ _ _ _

3. **Wordprints**

(a) The store owners on Maple Street held a lucky draw to raise money for the Humane Society. Pretend your name was picked. To win, you must write the missing List Words in this message:

Take a ⬜⬜⬜⬜⬜ and you may ⬜⬜⬜⬜⬜ the

lucky ⬜⬜⬜⬜ of a ⬜⬜⬜⬜⬜ ⬜⬜⬜⬜ collection.

(b) Use other List Words to write your own wordprint message about something you might like to buy or sell.

Writing Connections

1. **Shopping Around**

Choose three kinds of stores you like to visit and write a sentence to tell why you like to visit each of them.

2. **My Life as a Chess Set**

Pretend you are one of the following:

- an old chess set at a garage sale
- a puppy or kitten in a pet shop
- a pair of skates in a department store

Write a story to tell about:

(a) what you do while waiting for someone to buy you.

(b) who buys you, and why they buy you.

(c) what happens next.

Checkup
See how many List Words you can spell now.

22 Abracadabra!

lucky   wanted
dream   tale
wonder   ordered
such   chain
girl's   learned
yours   theirs
watched   our
wishes   friend's
asked

Your Class Words
Add words your class would like to learn to spell.

> **Checking What You Know**
> The chart on your Pretest will help you to see why you made any errors.

Meaning Connections

Tales of Magic

Unscramble the List Words to complete these sentences:

(1) The genie in the lamp granted Aladdin's siwshe.

(2) The wicked witch tadenw to eat Hansel and Gretel.

(3) Pinocchio awtehcd in horror as his nose grew longer.

(4) "What's in the basket?" the wolf sakde Little Red Riding Hood.

78

(5) The thunderbird was **ushc** a powerful creature that it could make thunder and lightning.

(6) The silver **inahc** turned to gold at King Midas' touch.

(7) In the **alet** of Rumpelstiltskin, a king **eordder** a girl to spin straw into gold.

Pattern Connections

1. **Whose Shoes**?

   Write sentences to complete the chart:

The shoes belong to her.	*They are her shoes.*	*The shoes are hers.*
The shoes belong to them.	*They are their shoes.*	(a)
The shoes belong to you.	(b)	(c)
The shoes belong to us.	(d)	(e)
The shoes belong to him.	(f)	(g)

2. **Sleeping Castles**

   (a) The people in the castles have been asleep for a hundred years. Break the spell by writing the words in each castle in alphabetical order.

   (1)
   wonder
   wishes
   wanted
   we

   (2)
   watched
   wanted
   walls
   waken
   wagon

   (3)
   wishes
   witch
   whose
   wind
   wonder

   (b) Use four of the words in sentences about magic.

3. **Whose Flying Carpet?**

The lamp **belonging to Aladdin** is Aladdin's lamp. Rewrite this story. Use **apostrophe** plus **s ('s)** to write the short form for each group of words printed like this.

A clever weaver made the carpet belonging to the girl. When the girl sat on the magic carpet, it flew her to a house belonging to a friend. The flight of the girl made her famous throughout the land.

4. **Magic Wand**

Be a word changer. Make ten different words by adding the endings to the words on the magic wand. Check in a dictionary to be sure you have made real words.

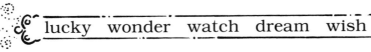

lucky   wonder   watch   dream   wish   learn

Writing Connections

1. **Three Wishes**

   If you were granted three wishes, what would you wish? Write three sentences that begin with I wish to tell what you would wish, and why.

2. **Wish, Come True!**

   Pretend that one of your wishes **has** come true. Write a paragraph to tell about it. Tell how it happened. What did **you** do to help make the wish come true? What did other people do?

   ▶ Exchange paragraphs with a partner to check the spelling and punctuation.

   > **Checkup**
   > Add any words you missed to your Personal Spelling Dictionary.

23 Now Hear This

bark   alarm   chirp   laughing
radio   drum   songs   weak
heard   hello   loudly   stairs
sea   creak   cries   noise
buzz

Your Class Words

Add up to five words to your list.

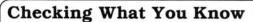

> **Checking What You Know**
> Underline the difficult parts of any
> words you missed on the Pretest.

Meaning Connections

1. **Sound Crossword**

   Use the meaning clues to write the List
   Words that solve the puzzle.

   Across

   2 a greeting
   4 a dog sound
   6 a kind of clock that rings

   Down

   1 a bird sound
   3 synonym for noisily
   4 a bee sound
   5 a squeaky stair sound

2. Why Is It?

Why is it that a doorbell has a **ring** but no fingers?

Write a List Word to complete each of these "Why is it?" questions:

Why is it that...

(a) a tree has _____ but no bite?

(b) a _____ plays but doesn't have fun?

(c) robins sing _____ but cannot talk?

(d) a _____ makes rolls but nobody eats them?

Pattern Connections

1. Telephone Poles

Homophones are words that sound the same but have different spellings and meanings. Use the telephone poles to help you write five List Words with their homophones (**Hint**: All the List Words are in the **a** pole.)

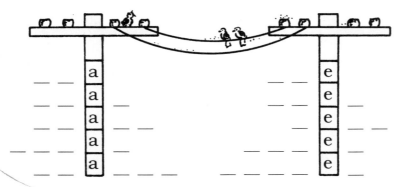

2. Letter Adder

(a) You can use **in** to make **something a bee does**:

   in *sting*

   Make List Words by adding one or more letters to the beginning and end of each word below.

   ear   on   ad   air   is

(b) Choose two of the words you wrote and use them in a sentence about something you might hear on the radio.

82

3. **Rhyme Time**

Copy the shapes below. Add letters to make crossword pairs that rhyme. The first pair is done for you.

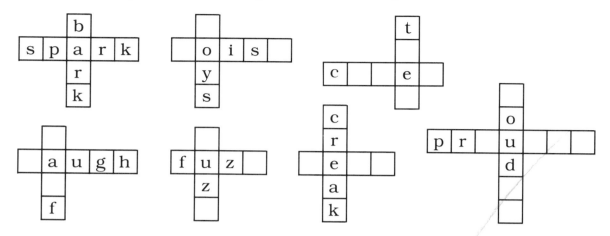

Writing Connections

1. **Did You Hear the Birch Bark?**

   Did you hear the thunder clap?
   No, but I heard the cloud burst.

   Write three more funny questions and answers. These words may give you some ideas.

   - diamond ring
   - telephone call
   - sugar bowl
   - shoe box
   - home run
   - board walk

2. **Sound Diary**

   What sounds did you hear yesterday? Write a Dear Diary entry, telling about four sounds you heard. Did someone call you to get up? Did you hear a plane or a train? What animals and birds did you hear? How did the sounds make you feel? Which did you like best? Why?

   > **Checkup**
   > Always add any words you need to study to your Personal Spelling Dictionary.

24 Backup

noise	laughing	sold	above	our
waited	such	watched	master	loudly
answer	stopped	peaches	wishes	monster
lucky	popcorn	ghost	chance	spend
seller	girl's	beside	ordered	friend's
bark	bought	belong	dead	foggy
hiding	buzz	creak	chain	sound
dream	hopped	ranch	songs	cries
owner	silver	between	become	running
radio	movie	paid	follow	sea
ponies	alarm	chirp	cherry	hello
closed	yours	tonight	pear	across
middle	deep	remained	learned	weak
heard	coin	wanted	boil	castle
wonder	drum	saved	theirs	asked
police	ticket	tale	cent	sign
whole	closer	chase	bushes	stairs

1. **Drop-a-Letter**

   You can often drop one letter in a word to make a new
   word. For example:

   witch   witc**h   with**
   hopped   hopp**ed   hoped**

   Find eight words that you can do
   this with. Look for them in the
   List Words, or in your Class Words.
   Write each word and the new word
   you can make by dropping a letter.

2. Twin Bill

Write the List Words that fit these clues. In each row, the letter in the box is the last letter in the first answer **and also** the first letter in the second answer. One row is done for you.

When you are finished, the letters in the pole should spell a name for a person in an adventure movie.

(a) small horses

(b) steps

(c) a spirit

(d) this evening

(e) ocean

(f) a kind of clock

(g) a beastlike creature

(h) a place to raise cattle

(i) a young sheep

(j) shrubs

(k) Hi

(l) commanded; directed

(m) full of fog

(n) belonging to you

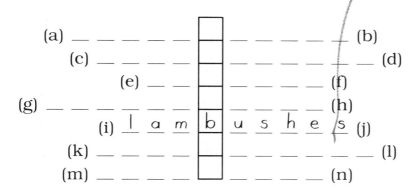

(a) _ _ _ _ _ [ ] _ _ _ _ _ (b)
(c) _ _ _ _ [ ] _ _ _ _ _ _ (d)
(e) _ _ [ ] _ _ _ _ (f)
(g) _ _ _ _ _ _ [ ] (h)
(i) l a m b u s h e s (j)
(k) _ _ _ _ [ ] _ _ _ _ _ _ (l)
(m) _ _ _ _ _ [ ] _ _ _ _ (n)

3. Ad Mix-up

Help! The spacing between the letters is wrong in these billboards. Write the messages as they should be.

BU YATIC KETF

ORAC HAN CET

OWI NARA DIO

SILV ERB OUG

HTA NDSO LD

WAN TE DAPO

PCOR NSEL LER

4. Castle Climb

There are three ladders to climb to get into the castle. All three have broken rungs. Each broken rung needs a List Word that keeps the alphabetical order. Fix each ladder by adding the missing List Words.

(1) above	(7)	(13)
(2)	(8) belong	(14)
(3)	(9)	(15) chase
(4) answer	(10)	(16)
(5)	(11) boil	(17)
(6) aunt	(12) bought	(18) closed

5. Fingerspelling

People sometimes use their fingers to spell out words.

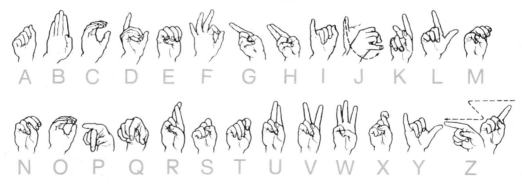

A B C D E F G H I J K L M

N O P Q R S T U V W X Y Z

(a) Write the List Words that the hand is spelling. They are all words that a person might use while shopping.

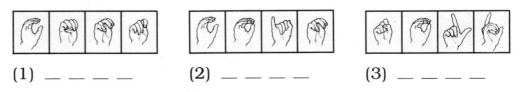

(1) _ _ _ _   (2) _ _ _ _   (3) _ _ _ _

(b) Choose three List Words. Practise using fingerspelling to spell them.

Wordworks

1. Dream Time

Cam dreamed about flying like a bird.

Nancy dreamed about swimming in the Olympics.

Pat dreamed about being the captain of a hockey team.

Think about dreams you have had. Write four sentences starting **I dreamed about**.

2. A Dream Story

Some dreams are like adventure stories. Have you had a dream like this? Write a story about one of your dreams. Who was in the dream? Where did it take place? What happened? How did you feel about what happened? If you wish, add new ideas to your dream story. Change it in any other way you like. Give your story an exciting title.

▶ Exchange stories with a partner to check the spelling and use of punctuation marks. Then reread your own story to see if you need to add action words and describing words to make it more exciting.

25 Dinosaur Days

dinosaur	age	earlier	rather
bottom	died	largely	appeared
different	nearly	sudden	hungry
matter	till	facts	huge
enemy			

Your Class Words

Add words that your class would like to learn to spell.

Checking What You Know

Use the Study Steps every day to learn new words.

Meaning Connections

Dinosaur Time Chart

Write List Words to complete the time chart:

About 225 to 65 million years ago...	About 64 million years ago to today...	Today...
a kind of animal called the __1__ lived on Earth. During that time, some dinosaurs lived __2__ they were over one hundred years old.	mammals __3__ on Earth. Dinosaurs __4__ out. Why? Was their main __5__ a change in the weather? Did they become __6__ and die for lack of food?	we can still learn many __7__ about dinosaurs. Their bodies have left clues in the form of fossils. Fossils help us to learn about a much __8__ time in our Earth's past.

88

Pattern Connections

1. **Earlier Days**

   (a) Help the baby dinosaur hatch from its egg. Make ten words by adding the endings on the egg to the words below. Check in a dictionary to be sure you have made real words.

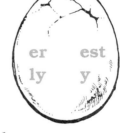

   | huge | final | hungry |
   | sudden | near | early |

   (b) Choose four of the words you made and use them in two sentences about dinosaurs.

2. **Huge, Terrible Lizards**

   Help the scientist collect words to use in a story about the "terrible lizards." Find and write:

   (a) the List Word and three other words with the **g** sound in **charge**.

   (b) the List Word and three other words with the **g** sound in **ugly**.

   (c) the List Word and three other words with the **th** sound in **mother**.

   (d) the List Word and two other words with the **ea** sound in **earth**.

   (e) the List Words and two other words with the **ea** sound in **fearsome**.

89

3. **What's in a Name?**

   (a) The word dinosaur comes from two Greek words: dino, which means "terrible," and sauro, which means "lizard." If dinosaur means "terrible lizard," what do you think Albertosaurus means?

   (b) The word terrible has double consonants. Write in alphabetical order the six List Words that have double consonants.

Writing Connections

1. **My Time Line**

   Scientists use a **time line** to show when events happened in the past. You can use a time line to show the important events in your life. For example:

Age	1	2	3	4	5	6	7
Event	walked	talked	rode a tricycle	got a puppy	brother born	read a book	got a bicycle

   Make a time line of the important events in **your** life so far.

2. **Make Your Own Dinosaur**

   Did you know that some dinosaurs were as small as chickens and others could fly like birds? Dinosaurs lived all over the world, and most were peaceful plant eaters. Some scientists believe that dinosaurs might have been brightly coloured—even striped!

   Make up your own amazing dinosaur. Give it an interesting name. Write a paragraph to tell about your dinosaur. What does it look like? How does it move? Where does it live and what does it eat?

   Checkup
   Add any words you had trouble with to your Personal Spelling Dictionary.
   ---

jungle elephant
mammals deer
foxes shut
key donkey
whale lie
paws cage
wolves monkey
goose fur
tiger

Your Class Words
Choose three more words to add to your list.

> **Checking What You Know**
> The Study Steps will help you to spell any words you missed.

Meaning Connections

Who Am I?

Solve the riddles by writing List Word animal names:

(a) A liger is a cross between me and a lion.

(b) I am the largest animal alive today.

(c) Along with foxes, we belong to the dog family.

(d) The Spanish name for me is burro.

(e) In an old story, I laid a golden egg.

(f) When I was a baby, I was called a fawn.

Pattern Connections

1. **More Animals Please**

   (a) Make each of the following animal names mean **more than one**. Complete the chart by writing the plurals in the lists where they belong.

   | fox | whale | goose | wolf | walrus | salmon |
   | donkey | deer | elephant | tiger | moose | monkey |

Add s	Add es	Change f to v —Add es	Change some letters in the middle	Don't change a thing
dolphins	*lynxes*	*calves*	*mice*	*sheep*

   (b) Use three of the new words you just wrote in sentences about animals you might see at the zoo.

2. **Animal Sounds**

   One of the underlined letter sounds is **not** the same as the sound of the other underlined letters in each group. Write the word that does not fit.

   (a) cougar, baboon, true, shut, tuna
   (b) laughing, elephant, doghouse, giraffe, fur
   (c) paws, cow, because, dog, crocodile
   (d) tiger, goose, cage, alligator, frogs
   (e) bear, beaver, deer, canary, anteater

3. **Zoo Trees**

   Make these trees taller to give more shade to the zoo animals. Do it by writing three more words that belong in each spelling pattern.

   gle — eagle, giggle
   ant — want, anteater
   aw — awful, squawk
   mal — normal, mallard
   key — hockey, turkey

4. **What Is in a Zoo?**

Imagine that your dictionary is divided into these three equal parts:

(1) a–h (2) i–p (3) q–z

(a) Write in alphabetical order the List Words that you would find in the a–h part.

(b) Write the List Words and two of your own animal words that would fit in the middle part.

(c) Write the List Words and three of your own words that would fit in q–z.

Writing Connections

1. **Animal Riddles**

**What has two humps and wanders around in the Arctic?
A lost camel.**

Try making up two more animal riddles of your own.

2. **What Do You Think?**

Should wild animals be kept in a zoo to protect them from hunters and other enemies? Are zoo animals unhappy about losing their freedom? Write a paragraph telling what **you** think about these questions.

Checkup
How many List Words can you spell now?

27 Dear World

rocky   creek
smooth   excuse
pollution   shady
garbage   dirty
salty   sandy
cities   smoke
coast   clean
island   useful
grew

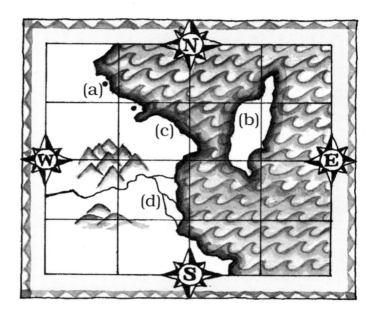

Your Class Words

Add three to five more words to your list.

> **Checking What You Know**
> Write the correct spellings of any words you
> missed on the Pretest.

Meaning Connections

1. **Map Words**

   Use List Words to label four things shown on the map.

2. **What Is It Like?**

   (a) Write the List Word that means almost the same as

       (1) stony   (3) stream   (5) forgive   (7) tidy
       (2) trash   (4) level   (6) seashore   (8) helpful

94

(b) Add another word to each List Word you wrote to make describing pairs. For example:

sandy beach

Pattern Connections

1. **U-Turns**

   Many words have the **long** u sound as in human. We spell this sound in different ways:

u	u_e	ew
curious	*huge*	*newspaper*

   (a) Find the List Words and three other words that have this u sound and write them under the correct spelling pattern.

   (b) Write two sentences about the beauty of nature that use words from your chart.

2. **The ness Islands**

   We can add the suffix ness to some describing words to make naming words. For example:

   The path was stony.
   We felt the stoniness of the path.

   (a) Add ness to each word and write it on the island where it belongs.

smoky	salty	rocky	cleanly
dirty	shady	sandy	useful

   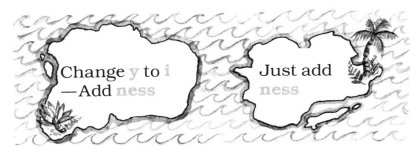

   Change y to i —Add ness   Just add ness

   (b) Use two of your ness words in two sentences.

3. **Pollution Solutions**

Complete the sentences with words that have the following spelling patterns. (**Hint**: Some of your answers will be List Words.) The first one is started for you.

tion (a) We should try to find _solutions_ to the problems of _____.

and (b) The _____ shores of the little _____ were sticky from the oil spill.

age (c) The mayor flew into a _____ at the sight of all the dirty _____ on the street.

use (d) It is more _____ to clean up pollution than to try to _____ ourselves for polluting.

oke (e) They _____ about the problem of too much _____ coming from the factory's chimneys.

Writing Connections

Thank you for not smoking.

Take nothing but pictures. Leave nothing but footprints.

1. **Signs and Slogans**

Our world is a beautiful place. What signs and slogans (sayings) have you seen about keeping it that way? List two you have seen or make up two signs or slogans of your own.

2. **Island in the Sun**

Suppose you could have an island of your own. Write a paragraph describing your island. What would be special about it? Would it have high mountains and volcanoes, or secret caves and paths? Why would you like to live there? Would other people like to visit? What could they see and do there? Give your island a name.

▶ Reread your paragraph to check your punctuation.

> **Checkup**
> See how many List Words you can spell now.

28 *Flying Free*

canary   butterflies
wings   robins
might   flies
hatch   beak
busy   feathers
aren't   body
cricket   spring
cannot   tail
bats

Your Class Words
Add words your class would
like to learn to spell.

Checking What You Know
Don't forget to use the Study Steps every day
to help you spell new words.

Meaning Connections

1. **Flying Word Webs**

   Copy these headings in your notebook and use List
   Words to complete the chart.

Names of flying creatures	Parts of flying creatures

Pattern Connections

1. **Butterflies Flutter By**

   (a) *The dragonfly sat on the tailgate of the truck.*

   Which words in the sentence were made by joining two words? Use the following words to write seven more compound words.

   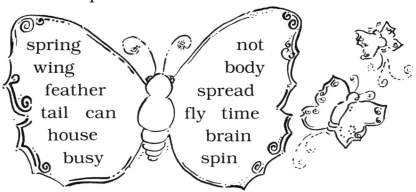

   spring
   wing
   feather
   tail   can
   house
   busy

   not
   body
   spread
   fly   time
   brain
   spin

   (b) Check in a dictionary to be sure that all the words you made are real compounds.

   (c) Use three of your compounds in sentences about flying or flying creatures.

2. **Flywheels Don't Fly**

   (a) **Apostrophes** (') can be used to show that words have been shortened. **Don't** is the short form for **do not**. What is the short form for **is not**?

   (b) Use short forms to complete the chart.

   (c) Use a dictionary to check the spelling of your short forms.

Long form	Short form
are not	(1)
was not	(2)
were not	(3)
have not	(4)
had not	(5)
cannot	(6)
could not	(7)

3. **Letter Adder**

You can use **in** to make **something to fly with**.

in—*wings*

Make List Words by adding one or more letters to the beginning and end of each word below.

bin   lie   an   us   at   in   rick   hat

Writing Connections

1. **Call Me Chickadee**

chickadee   hawk   woodpecker   loon   eagle

How many bird names do you know? List five of your favourites. Use three of your bird names in sentences.

2. **Poems Can Fly**

Housefly	Returning robins
Horsefly	Twigs
Firefly	String
Dragonfly—	Nest
Fly away from me!	Five blue eggs
	Spring is here!

Use naming words to write your own list poem about flying or things that fly. Give your poem an interesting title.

▸ Reread your poem to see if you need to change any of the words to make it more exciting.

> **Checkup**
> Always add any words you miss to your Personal Spelling Dictionary.

29 Trees Please

pine   leaves   putting
cone   bare   berries
bunch   cutting   birch
root   blossom   climb
thick   planting   ground
maple   branch

Your Class Words

Add three to five words to the list.

Checking What You Know

The chart on your Pretest will help you to see why you made errors.

Meaning Connections

1. **Up in a Tree**

Write the List Words that complete this story:

One day Amyra's kitten thought he would __1__ up a tree to look at a robin's nest. In a sweet-smelling pink __2__, he saw a bumblebee. Clinging to a thick tree __3__, the kitten looked down and saw Amyra's mom __4__ the grass. He saw Amyra __5__ out the garbage and her dad __6__ a small tree with tiny red __7__ on it.

Suddenly the kitten began to howl because he could not get back down to the __8__. So Amyra and her mom had to use the ladder to help the frightened kitten down.

2. Tree Leaves

(a) Copy this chart and use List Words to complete it:

Kinds of trees	Parts of trees

(b) Add three more words to each column.

Pattern Connections

1. Leafy Letters

Each numbered leaf stands for a letter in a List Word. The clue will help you to figure out what some of the letters are. Add the missing letters and write the List Word. The letters in the boxes will name a food that grows on trees.

Code	Clue	List Word
(a) 1 2 3 4	321 spells nip.	☐ _ _ _
(b) 1 2 3 4 5 6	51456 spells elves.	_ ☐ _ _ _ _
(c) 1 2 3 4 5 6	5231 spells crab.	_ _ ☐ _ _ _
(d) 1 2 3 4 5	521 spells hub.	_ _ _ ☐ _
(e) 1 2 3 4 5	1345 spells tick.	_ ☐ _ _ _
(f) 1 2 3 4 5	3245 spells pale.	_ _ _ _ ☐
(g) 1 2 3 4 5 6 7	7654 spells moss.	_ _ _ _ ☐ _ _

2. Bursting into Bloom

Watch the root word wood explode:

woodlike   woods   woody   wood   wooded   woodier
woodless   woodiest

Explode these root words to make new words:

leaf   plant   thick

101

3. **Branching Out**

Add an ending to each word printed like this to make it fit the sentence. Rewrite the sentences using the new words you have made.

(a) leaf, branch   We could not see nests among the _____ because of the many _____.

(b) cut, maple   They collected maple sap by _____ small slits in the bark of all the _____ on their farm.

(c) bunch, berry   She picked _____ of purple _____.

(d) bare, bare   The tree began to look bare when the leaves started to fall. It looked even _____ when the wind started to blow. The tree looked _____ of all in the middle of winter.

Writing Connections

1. **Where Does Chocolate Grow?**

Write sentences about five more foods that come from trees.

2. **Treehouse Restaurant**

(a) Help the owners plan their restaurant. Write sentences to tell where a Treehouse Restaurant might be and what it might look like.

(b) **Fresh Peach Dumplings with Rich Maple Syrup**
Tasty Almond Cake with Sprinkles of Cinnamon

What other desserts could the Treehouse Restaurant serve? Write menu descriptions for four desserts. Try to include two foods from trees in each dessert.

Checkup
Record any words you missed in your Personal Spelling Dictionary.

dinosaur	earlier	might	dirty	cities
rocky	mammals	deer	beak	wings
pine	planting	hatch	donkey	cage
canary	shady	key	smoke	body
jungle	robins	thick	enemy	clean
died	leaves	matter	paws	hungry
smooth	foxes	salty	age	putting
cone	different	busy	coast	monkey
butterflies	sandy	whale	bunch	huge
nearly	root	aren't	cricket	maple
tiger	creek	berries	wolves	useful
goose	feathers	sudden	island	spring
flies	elephant	bottom	rather	blossom
grew	bats	pollution	garbage	fur
till	shut	cannot	lie	climb
branch	largely	birch	cutting	tail
bare	excuse	facts	appeared	ground

1. **Tree Puzzle**

   Each word below is part of a List Word. Add the missing letters and write the List Words. The first one is done for you. The letters in the trees should spell the name of a person who helps protect forests from fires and other dangers.

   (a) use f u l

   (b) _ 🌲 _ key

   (c) mat _ _ 🌲

   (d) differ 🌲 _ _

   (e) _ 🌲 land

   (f) can _ _ 🌲

   (g) but _ _ _ _ _ _ 🌲 _

   (h) ear _ _ _ 🌲

103

2. Animal Scrambles

Unscramble the letters printed like this in each question to make a List Word. Then answer each riddle by using another List Word plus a rhyming word. The first one is done for you.

(a) What do you call a water bird that has escaped from its **geca**? *geca = cage*
answer: *a loose goose*

(b) What time is it when a **omneyk** goes up a tree?
answer: _____ time

(c) What do **xfoes** do when they are tired?
answer: take a pause to rest their _____

(d) What is another name for a feeble nose on a **nacyar**?
answer: a weak _____

(e) What do you call a **arreth** nasty insect?
answer: a wicked _____

(f) What is another name for a faded mammal that lives in the **ase**?
answer: a pale _____

(g) What do you call the hair on a female **grtie**?
answer: her _____

3. Mystery Sentences

Complete the mystery sentences. Use these List Words in alphabetical order:

key	creek	sudden	dinosaur
appeared	tiger	bottom	maple
shady	spring	smooth	island

(a) It _____ that, at the _____ of the _____ , the scientists had found _____ fossils.

(b) On the _____ , we learned that the word _____ is a name for a _____ seed.

(c) They were under that _____ tree near the _____ rock last _____ when, all of a _____ , they saw a hungry _____ .

104

4. This Is the Ending, My Friend

s   es   er   y   ful   tion   ing

Complete this puzzle with List Words that use the endings. For some, you may need to add one of the endings.

Across

1 snipping with something sharp
3 what ocean water is
6 dirtying of air, water, or soil
7 sly animals that look like small dogs
9 opposite of friends
10 at a time closer to the start
11 feeling hunger
12 can be used

Down

1 like towns but bigger
2 comes out of an egg
4 person who climbs
5 large wild members of the dog family
6 putting seeds into the ground
8 trees with white bark

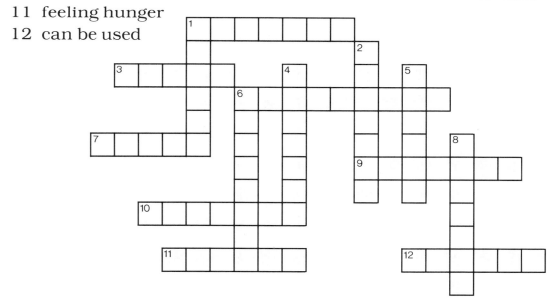

5. Word Stairs

Keep the stairs going. Use the last letter in a List Word to start a new List Word.

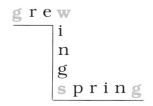

g r e w
    i
    n
    g
s p r i n g

Wordworks

1. **What Was It?**

   "I saw a strange creature at the zoo," said Tanya. "I don't know what it was."

   "Was it bigger than a dog?" asked Max. "What colour was it?"

   (a) Help Max find out more about Tanya's creature. Write five more questions he could ask her.

   (b) Choose an animal that Tanya might have seen. Write the answers to all of Max's questions.

2. **Honk If You Have Webbed Feet**

   Debra used words telling about a goose to write her goose poem.

   Write an animal picture poem of your own without naming the animal. The following shapes may give you some ideas.

31 Now We're Getting Somewhere

highway   helicopter   load   rail
runway   airplane   pulled   paved
driving   ambulance   wheel   road
go-cart   automobile   drove   goes
corner

Your Class Words
Add up to five words
to your list.

Checking What You Know
The chart on your Pretest will help
you to see why you made any errors.

Meaning Connections

Making Your Way

Complete this travel
puzzle in your notebook.
Write the List Words that
are **synonyms** for the
clues.

Across	Down
2 freeway	1 operating
5 crossroad	3 car
7 moves	4 hoop
8 aircraft	6 dragged

107

Pattern Connections

1. **Word Wheelies**

   You can use these compounds to make "word wheelies":

   go-cart
   cartload

   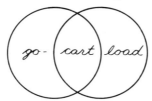

   streetcar
   carport
   porthole

   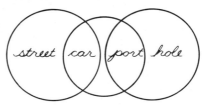

   (a) Use List words or parts of List Word compounds to complete these new compounds:

   (a) _____ road   (d) _____ barrow   (g) cart _____

   (b) boat _____   (e) _____ side   (h) rail _____

   (c) _____ chair   (f) _____ mail

   (b) Make four "word wheelies" of your own. Use the compounds that you wrote and these compounds.

runway	boxcar	houseboat	shipyard
wayside	roadhouse	signpost	chairlift
sidewalk	postmark	mailbox	

2. **Lost Travellers**

   Lost travellers tramped part of a message in the snow. Write the List Words that complete the message.

   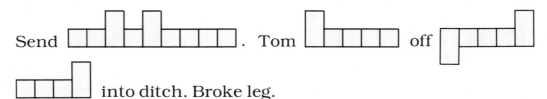

   Send [ ] . Tom [ ] off [ ]

   [ ] into ditch. Broke leg.

3. **Helicopter Words**

   How many words can you make out of the letters in the word helicopter? Write all the words you can make.

108

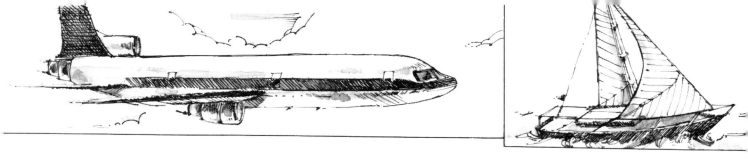

4. **Shortcuts**

   (a) Write List Words for the short forms printed like this in the following sentence:

   Leaving their auto near the runway, the detectives jumped into their plane.

   (b) Now write the short forms for the following words:

   bicycles   tricycles   gasoline   taxicab   radiator

   (c) Choose two short forms and use them in a sentence about travelling.

Writing Connections

1. **Fast-moving Words**

   The automobile sped along the highway.

   Choose three other things that are **fast** and for each write a sentence to tell **how** it moves and **where** it travels.

2. **How Do You Get to School?**

   Sylvan walks to school.
   Jan goes in a wheelchair.

   How do **you** get to school? Write a paragraph or two to tell about it. When do you leave for school? What do you see and hear along the way? How long does it take? Answer some or all of these questions in your story.

   ▶ Reread your story to see if you can make it more interesting by using and, but, or, because, or while to join short sentences.

   ┌───┐
   │ **Checkup**   │
   │ Can you spell all the List Words now?   │
   └───┘

32 Farm Fresh

sheep   straw
cattle   post
wheat   calf
lamb   sleeping
trying   mare
colt   they're
weeds   their
barn   chicken
gallop

Your Class Words
Choose three to five more words to add to your list.

> **Checking What You Know**
> Write the correct spellings of any words you missed.

Meaning Connections

1. **Sunny Side Up**

   Use List Words to complete the farm family's job list:

   Leslie—Go to the ___1___ and milk the cows.
   Marie—Go to the ___2___ coop and gather the eggs.
   Dad—Go to the field and harvest ___3___.
   Mom—Ride the black mare into the pasture to fix the broken fence ___4___.
   Grandma and Grandpa—Shear the three white ___5___ and clean the wool.

2. **Whose Kid Is That?**

Write List Words to complete this animal-family chart:

Animals	Mother	Father	Baby
goats	*ewe*	*ram*	*kid*
(a)	ewe	ram	(b)
horses	(c)	stallion	(d)
(e)	cow	bull	(f)
(g)	hen	rooster	chick

3. **Over Where?**

(a) Words that sound the same but have different spellings and meanings are called **homophones**. Write the homophone that fits each meaning below:

   (1) belonging to them   (2) they are   (3) in that place

(b) Write three sentences about life on a farm. Use the three words you wrote in (**a**) in your sentences.

Pattern Connections

1. **Milkshake**

Watch the root word milk explode:

milked milker milks = milk = milky milking

Explode these words to make new words:

weed   sleep   try

2. **Tongue Twister Time**

Should sheep sleep in a shed?

Use List Words to write three tongue twisters of your own. You might like to use some of these words:

she	which	banging	wolves	willow	children
clover	clever	black	crept	Wednesday	

111

3. **Hat Full of Hay**

Here's how to change your cap into food for cattle:

h a [t]   h a [y]

Use the clues and make letter changes to complete the following chart. (**Hint**: The missing words on the right are all List Words.)

(a) dog sound	*bark*	?	farm animal home
(b) crow sound	*caw*	?	dried grain stems
(c) paying for	?	?	making an effort
(d) fourth planet	?	?	female horse or donkey
(e) ship's kitchen	*galley*	?	horse's fastest way of running

Writing Connections

1. **Oh Where, Oh Where?**

   "The sheep's in the meadow,
     The cow's in the corn."

   Name three other farm animals. Write sentences to tell where you might see them on a farm.

2. **Chicken in the Window**

   Chicken in the window.
   Turkey in the straw.
   Crow sits on the fence post.
   Caw! Caw! Caw!

   Write your own four-line poem
   about animals on a farm.

> **Checkup**
> Add any words you had trouble with to your Personal Spelling Dictionary.

112

33 How Are You?

danger   chest
alive   pump
I've   heal
fingers   should
heart   we'll
ill   tooth
she's   I'll
mind   care
won't

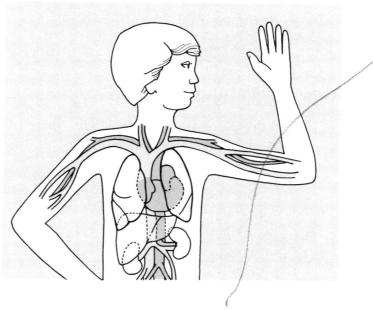

Your Class Words

What three words would your class like to add to the list?

Checking What You Know

The Study Steps will help you to spell any words you missed.

Meaning Connections

A Message from a Friend

Write the List Words that mean the same or almost the same as the words printed like this.

From inside your upper body, I push blood from your brain down to your toes. When you cut one of the digits on your hand, my blood rushes to help it get better. I feed each molar in your mouth and give your

continued on the next page. . .   113

legs energy to run away from harm. Without me, you would never get well when you are sick. You wouldn't even be able to stay living. So eat well and get lots of exercise to keep me strong.

Your friend, the body pump

Pattern Connections

1. **Keeping Safe and Well**

   (a) Write the new words you can make by adding the endings to the List Words on the toothbrush.

   | tooth care danger heart |

   (b) Use the new words to complete these sentences.

   (1) We should be _____ to eat foods that are good for us.

   (2) Only a _____ person would cross a street without watching for cars.

   (3) If we don't take care of our teeth, we might someday find ourselves _____.

   (4) The edge of a steep cliff is a _____ place to play.

   (5) Only a _____ person would refuse to help a sick child.

2. **Healthwise**

   (a) Find the four List Words that have a th, ch, or sh pattern and add them to the chart.

th	ch	sh
think	teach	share
health	chicken	wash

   (b) Complete each column in the chart by adding three other words.

   (c) Choose three words from your chart and use each in a sentence about taking care of your health.

114

3. **Words in Our Mouths**

   (a) Shouldn't is the short form for should not. Write the short form for will not. Is it made the same way?

   (b) Write short forms for the following. Put each short form in the speech balloon where it belongs.

I have	we will	are not	he is	I will
she is	we are	they are	you have	

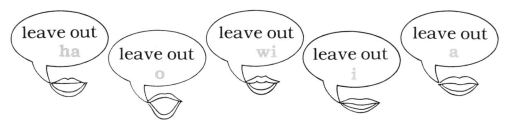

   (c) Add one more short form to three of the balloons.

Writing Connections

1. **The Three Sillies**

   The Three Sillies are tiny creatures who always have health and safety problems. Once they tried to catch a ride on an owl's back, but it bit them. One snowy day the Three Sillies went outdoors without their jackets. They all caught bad colds.

   Write sentences about three other problems the Three Sillies might have.

2. **Words from the Heart**

   Look back at "A Message from a Friend" on page 113. If you could have a conversation with **your** heart, what would you ask it? What might it tell you? Write your imaginary conversation and give it an interesting title.

   ▶ Exchange your story with a partner to check the use of quotation marks and other punctuation.

   > **Checkup**
   > See how many List Words you can spell now.

34 Play Ball!

prize   sports   tenth
strike   batter   club
twice   won   stole
match   reached   third
finish   sliding   first
raced   dropped

Your Class Words
Add three to five words that
your class would like to spell.

Checking What You Know
See how many of the words
you already know.

Meaning Connections

1. **Baseball Facts**

   Write List Words to complete this baseball fact sheet:

   (a) Like some other _____ , baseball is played on a field.

   (b) A batter may swing _____ without hitting the ball.
   But on the _____ strike, the batter is out.

   (c) A batter who hits the ball runs to _____ base.

   (d) A batter who has safely run around the bases and
   _____ home plate has scored a run.

   (e) At the end, the team with the most runs has _____
   the game.

2. **Batter Up**

Some words have more than one meaning. Write the List Word for each meaning below. Then write a second meaning for the same word. If you need help, use your Mini-Dictionary.

(a) baseball player who is batting   (c) heavy stick of wood

(b) game or contest

Pattern Connections

1. **Home Stretch**

   (a) Sometimes small words are inside bigger ones. Use the clues to write a small word for the first column. Now write the List Word that has the small word inside it. The first one is done for you.

(1) frozen water	*ice*	*twice*
(2) a rug	m _ _ _	_ _ _ _ _ _
(3) part of a fish	f _ _	_ _ _ _ _ _
(4) a harbour	p _ _ _	_ _ _ _ _ _
(5) a pot's top	l _ _	_ _ _ _ _ _ _
(6) used when camping	t _ _ _	_ _ _ _ _ _

   (b) Find three other List Words that have small words inside them. Write each word, write a meaning clue for the small word, and write the small word.

2. **Who's on First?**

   We use number words like eighth and fifth to tell about the order of things. For example:

   Our team has won seven games.

   We play our eighth game today.

   Write the numbers from one to ten down the left-hand side of your notebook. Beside each, write its order word. Like this:

   two – second

3. **Home Run**

Write the past form of each of these action words. (**Hint**: Some past forms do *not* end in *ed*.) When you are finished, use the letters in the bases to write the name of a player who catches fly balls.

(a) win   (c) bat   (e) slide   (g) steal   (i) reach
(b) strike   (d) finish   (f) race   (h) drop   (j) prize

(a) _ □ _   (f) _ _ _ □ _
(b) _ _ _ □ _ _   (g) _ _ _ □ _
(c) _ _ _ □ _ _   (h) □ _ _ _ _ _ _
(d) □ _ _ _ _ _ _ _   (i) _ □ _ _ _ _ _
(e) _ _ □ _   (j) _ □ _ _ _ _

Writing Connections

1. **Baseball Fact Sheet**

   Look back at the Baseball Facts on page 116. Write three more facts to add to the baseball fact sheet.

2. **Say Hey!**

   A famous baseball player called Willie Mays was nicknamed the Say Hey Kid. This was because he used to yell "Say Hey!" to his friends. Many other baseball players have had nicknames:

   Icehouse Wilson (George Peacock Wilson)
   The Hawk (Andre Dawson)

   Write a story about how a baseball player might have gotten a certain nickname. You can choose a real nickname or make one up.

   > **Checkup**
   > Always add any words you need to study to your Personal Spelling Dictionary.

35 Sailing into Summer

hours   news
stern   shells
waves   delay
sailing   self
hotel   broken
stayed   skipping
stream   swam
hottest   summer
daylight

Your Class Words
Add words your class would like to learn to spell.

Checking What You Know
The Study Steps will help you spell any words you missed.

Meaning Connections

Off to the Turtle Races

Rewrite the following story. Change each word printed like this to the List Word that is its **antonym** (opposite).

    It was the coldest day of our winter holidays. In the zoo's aquarium stood a tub full of turtles. Marcel and I watched a brown one as it slowly sank through the water. "Come to the turtle races," said a big sign. "Don't hurry!"

Pattern Connections

1. **Our Shellfish**

   (a) We went on a sailing holiday by ourselves. Use the words on the crab's shell to write eight more words ending with **self** or **selves**.

   (b) Choose two words ending in **self** or **selves**. Use them in two sentences about summer holidays.

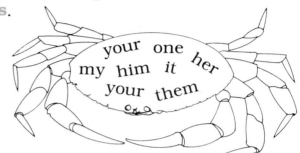

2. **Three's a Crowd**

   Complete each group of three by making changes in a List Word so that it fits with the other two words. The first one is done for you.

   (a) stream, *streaming*, streamed

   (b) _____, skipping, skipped

   (c) delay, _____, delayed

   (d) _____, breaking, broken

   (e) swim, _____, swam

   (f) sail, sailing, _____

   (g) stay, _____, stayed

3. **All Sails Set**

   For each sail, write the List Words with the same spelling pattern.

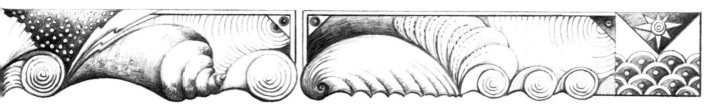

4. Gone Fishing

Help Rosa and Paolo get ready to go on vacation by writing the words in each trunk in alphabetical order:

(a)

swam	self	shells
sailing	stern	summer
stayed	stream	skipping

(b)

hours	hotel
hottest	holiday

Writing Connections

1. Summerlike

I like going to the beach, but I don't like getting a sunburn.

I like going to the cottage, but I don't like mosquitoes.

Think of three things you will probably do this summer. Use your ideas to write three sentences that follow this pattern:

I like. . .but I don't like. . .

2. Calendar Diary

Make a calendar for July of this year. In one colour, such as red, write things you **hope** to do on different days in July.

Take your calendar home. As you go through the month of July, use another colour, such as blue, to write what you **really** do on different days. You might not want to write on your calendar every day. But keep a record of the most important things!

> **Checkup**
> Can you spell all the List Words now?

danger	lamb	stream	heal	skipping
hours	go-cart	barn	ambulance	tenth
sheep	fingers	we'll	wheat	driving
highway	sailing	airplane	reached	tooth
prize	finish	stole	self	their
shells	mare	hottest	pulled	swam
runway	corner	won't	should	club
alive	heart	straw	sliding	I'll
won	hotel	strike	sleeping	road
cattle	colt	chest	paved	batter
stern	raced	load	trying	summer
calf	ill	daylight	automobile	care
wheel	stayed	post	broken	goes
twice	sports	pump	mind	chicken
I've	weeds	news	dropped	third
match	helicopter	drove	rails	gallop
waves	she's	delay	they're	first

1. **What Sharp Teeth You Have!**

   A mouse in the baseball players' dressing room chewed up
   a pitcher's letter from home. Put the word parts together to
   write six key words from the letter.

2. Letter Ladder

What surprising thing did Esther find in the hayloft at the farm? To find out, write the past or present forms of the action words. The first one is done for you.

(a) past form of goes

(b) past form of break

(c) past form of steal

(d) past form of try

(e) present form of swam

(f) present form of won

(g) present form of cared

(h) past form of reach

(i) past form of stay

(j) present form of cornered

(a) w e [n] t

(b) _ _ [ ] _ _

(c) _ [ ] _ _ _

(d) _ _ _ [ ] _

(e) _ _ [ ] _

(f) _ _ [ ]

(g) _ [ ] _ _

(h) _ _ _ [ ] _ _ _

(i) _ _ [ ] _ _ _

(j) _ _ _ [ ] _ _

3. The Back-to-Front Code

(a) In this code, sheep is **eepshay** and stream is **eamstray**.

(b) Decode the following messages:

   (1) Our ackblay aremay ashay a ewnay oltcay.

   (2) Icetway atthay atterbay olestay a asebay.

   (3) In ummersay eway avehay oremay aylightday ourshay.

(c) Write two messages of your own in the code. See if a friend can decode them.

4. **A Letter from Toby**

Help Toby write his letter. For each blank, write a List Word that is a **homophone** for one of the following words:

heel   ours   their   rode
one   mined   pries   aisle

Benson Ridge
June 11, 19 __

Dear Ms. Hind and Class,

   Lucky me! I __1__ first __2__ in the long-jump contest. But I sprained my ankle, so Mom drove me to the doctor. We were on the __3__ for over two __4__ because of the heavy traffic.

   "Never __5__ about taking off your jacket," said the doctor. "Let's have a look at that ankle."

   The doctor said that my ankle was going to __6__ all right, but __7__ have to stay home from school for a while. See you all soon.

Your classmate,
Toby

5. **Word Search**

Find and write 16 List Words that you could use to write about travelling. The words go down and across. The first word is sailing.

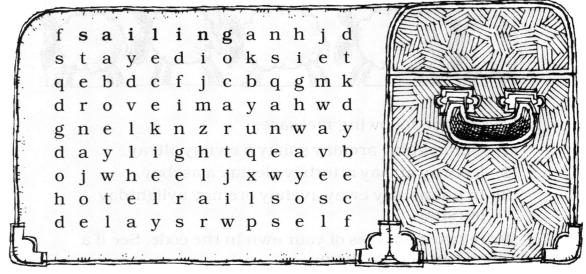

```
f s a i l i n g a n h j d
s t a y e d i o k s i e t
q e b d c f j c b q g m k
d r o v e i m a y a h w d
g n e l k n z r u n w a y
d a y l i g h t q e a v b
o j w h e e l j x w y e e
h o t e l r a i l s o s c
d e l a y s r w p s e l f
```

124

Wordworks

1. **Word Webs**

   (a) Complete this word web. Say the word summer to yourself, and then write two words it makes you think of. Now write two words for each of the two words you just wrote.

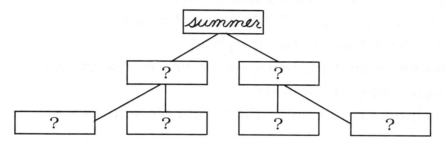

   (b) Make your own word webs for two of these words:

   wheel   danger   sailing   airplane

2. **Summer Here and Summer There**

   home   beach   mountains   Grandpa's house
   Yukon   farm   city   camp   exhibition

   Write down four places where you or your classmates may spend time this summer. Write a few sentences telling how to get to one of these places and why you would like to be there. Draw a map to help show how you get there.

Revising and Editing Guide

1. Revising

A.—For Authors

Here are some things to think about when you decide to revise the first draft of your work:

1. Did you write what you wanted to say?
2. What was the purpose of this piece of writing?
3. How well does it meet that purpose?
4. Will this piece be interesting for someone else to read?
5. Who might enjoy reading it?
6. What feelings do you have about this piece as you reread it?

B.—For Readers

Here are some things to look for when you are reading a classmate's writing and suggesting ways to make it better:

1. Can you guess why the author wrote this piece?
2. Did the author meet that purpose?
3. Is there any part you would like to know more about?
4. Did the beginning make you want to read more?
5. What held your interest as you read through to the end?
6. Is there any part you would like the author to make clearer?
7. How did this piece make you feel as you read it?

2. Editing

Here are some things to look for when you are checking a classmate's work, or when you are checking your own work:

1. Are all the events or steps written in order?
2. Could more or better **action words** and **describing words** be used to make the piece more interesting?
3. Does each **paragraph** (group of sentences) tell about one main idea?
4. Does each paragraph have a strong first sentence?
5. Could some of the short sentences be joined by using words such as **and**, **but**, **or**, **while**, **when**, and **because**?
6. Should some longer sentences be rewritten as shorter sentences?
7. Does the piece need a title?
8. Are all of the words spelled correctly? Use a dictionary to check any words that you think may be spelled incorrectly.
9. Does each sentence start with a capital letter?
10. **Proper names** (of persons and places) should start with capital letters. Does each proper name start with a capital?
11. Sentences that are statements end with **periods**. Does each statement end with a period?
12. Sentences that ask questions end with **question marks** (**?**). Does each question end with a question mark?
13. Are **commas** (,), **quotation marks** (" "), and other punctuation marks used correctly?
14. Each new paragraph should be **indented** (begin a few spaces from the left-hand margin). Is each paragraph indented?
15. Is the handwriting or printing clear and easy to read?

Superconnections

1. ABC's of Camping

(a) Use the clues to write four-letter words to complete this camping puzzle. (**Hint**: The answers will be in alphabetical order.)

(1) a wide space   a r e a

(2) large forest animal   __ __ __ __

(3) shelter in a mountain   __ __ __ __

(4) a timid forest animal   __ __ __ __

(5) a rabbit has long ones   __ __ __ __

(6) a burning flame   __ __ __ __

(7) camping equipment   __ __ __ __

(8) a walk through the woods   __ __ __ __

(9) one thing in a group   __ __ __ __

(10) a hot summer month   __ __ __ __

(b) Continue the ABC's of camping. Write clues that will complete the alphabet puzzle. The answers can have any number of letters. Ask a friend to solve it.

2. Space Search

There are 20 space-age words hidden in the puzzle. They go down and across. Find all 20 and you are ready for lift-off. The first word is astronaut.

s	a	s	t	r	o	n	a	u	t	m	t	m
p	p	u	m	o	o	n	b	l	y	a	x	r
a	l	n	s	t	a	r	o	e	a	r	t	h
c	v	e	s	s	e	l	v	b	o	s	z	p
e	c	a	p	s	u	l	e	r	a	d	a	r
s	r	m	a	v	l	a	n	d	i	n	g	r
h	o	r	y	c	o	u	n	t	d	o	w	n
i	c	b	l	u	m	n	p	l	a	n	e	t
p	k	v	o	c	t	c	l	o	u	d	s	t
c	e	b	a	l	o	h	s	p	a	c	e	z
b	t	o	d	g	a	l	a	x	y	t	y	v

128

3. Food for Thought

Many of our words for food have come from other languages. Use the clues about the origins of food names to complete the puzzle.

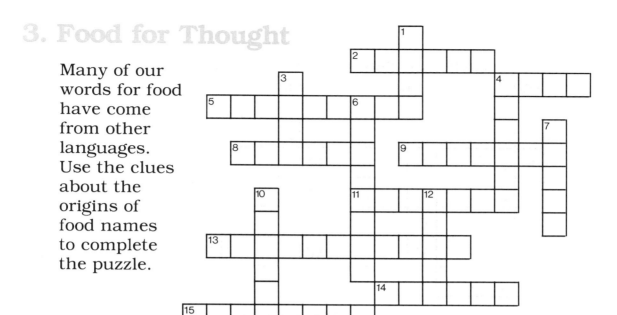

Across

2 The Persian word nārang named this juicy fruit.

4 The Old English word korn named this grain.

5 From the Latin word vegetabilis, meaning "growing."

8 From the Spanish word batata; made into chips.

9 The Greek word pēpon, meaning "ripened in the sun," named this Hallowe'en ornament.

11 From the Old North French word caboche, meaning "head"; looks like lettuce.

13 The Italian word cavolfiore, meaning "cabbage flower," named this vegetable.

14 From the Latin word radix, meaning "root."

15 This umbrella-shaped fungus gets its name from a Middle French word, mousseron.

Down

1 The Greek word daktylos named this fruit.

3 The Middle English word mete rhymes with our word.

4 Koekje is the Dutch word for this little, crisp cake.

6 The Italian word brocco named this vegetable.

7 The Latin word union named this teary vegetable.

10 Askútasquash is the Algonkian word for this vegetable.

12 From an Old English word, brēowan, meaning "to brew"; used to make a sandwich.

4. Morse Code

Morse Code uses dots and dashes to send messages. Each letter of the alphabet has its own pattern.

A	. _	B	_ . . .	C	_ . _ .	D	_ . .	E	.
F	. . _ .	G	_ _ .	H	. . . .	I	. .	J	. _ _ _
K	_ . _	L	. _ . .	M	_ _	N	_ .	O	_ _ _
P	. _ _ .	Q	_ _ . _	R	. _ .	S	. . .	T	_
U	. . _	V	. . . _	W	. _ _	X	_ . . _	Y	_ . _ _
Z	_ _ . .								

Here is a message using Morse Code:

/ . _ . / _ _ _ / . _ / _ . . /   ROAD

/ . . _ . / . _ . . / _ _ _ / _ _ _ / _ . . / . / _ . . /   FLOODED

(a) Use Morse Code to decode these messages

(1) / . _ . . / . _ / _ . / _ . . / . . . / . _ _ / . . / _ . . / . /

/ _ . . . / . _ . . / _ _ _ / _ . _ . / _ _ _ / . . / _ . / _ _ . /

/ . _ . / _ _ _ / . _ / _ . . /

/ . _ / . . . . / . / _ . / _ . . /

(2) / _ . . . / . /

/ _ . _ . / . _ / . _ . / . / . _ . . / . . _ / . _ . . /

/ . . _ . / . _ / . _ . . / . _ . . / . . / _ . / _ _ . /

/ . _ . / _ _ _ / _ . _ . / _ . _ / . . . . /

(3) / . . . / . . _ / _ . /   / . _ _ / . . / _ . . . / _ . . /

/ . . . / . . . . / . . / _ . / . /

/ – / – – – / – · · / · – / – · – – /

(4) / – – – / · · · – / · / · – · / – · – · / · – / · · · / – /

/ · · · / – · – / · · / · / · · · /

/ – / – – – / – – / – – – / · – · / · – · / – – – / · – – /

(b) Make up three of your own messages using Morse Code.

5. Limericks

A **limerick** is a funny poem that has five lines. The first, second, and fifth lines rhyme and have three beats each. The third and fourth lines rhyme and have two beats each. For example:

My funny big brother named Lou,
Tried to find a job he could do,
So he searched all around,
Till he finally found,
A job helping chimps at the zoo.

—Kirsten G., Grade 4

(a) Complete these limericks. Write the words you think will fit in the spaces.

I know a young runner named Dwight,
Who could run much faster than _____ ,
In a race he'd run,
Like a shot from a _____ ,
And finish on the previous _____ .

I have a pet dog named Brice,
Who likes to chase little white _____ ,
Under the stairs,
And around the _____ ,
He's only ever caught one _____ .

(b) Make up two of your own limericks.

131

6. Jumbo School-Day Crossword

Use the clues to complete this jumbo crossword about some of the things you do, see, and use at school. When you are done, unscramble the letters in the circles to answer this question:

Where do you have fun outside?

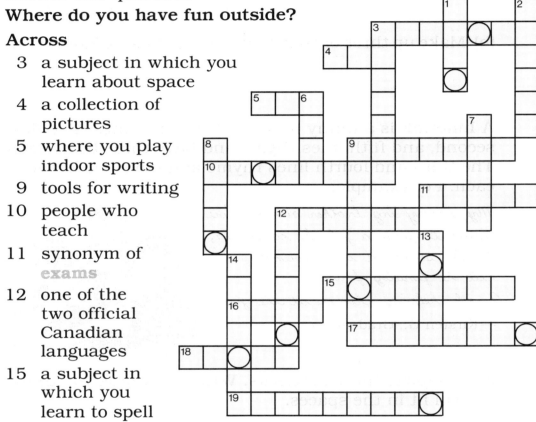

Across

3 a subject in which you learn about space

4 a collection of pictures

5 where you play indoor sports

9 tools for writing

10 people who teach

11 synonym of exams

12 one of the two official Canadian languages

15 a subject in which you learn to spell

16 to use your voice

17 what you are doing in school

18 you read stories in these

19 the month when school begins

Down

1 it rings at the end of the day

2 a short break

3 you write or read these

6 a subject in which you learn about numbers

7 a group of students

8 to prepare for a test

9 the head of your school

12 synonym of pals

13 it helps you draw a straight line

14 you study these; contains the small word son

7. Sounds the Same

(a) Complete these sentences using **homophones** (words that sound the same but are spelled differently). For example:

Her son likes to play outside in the sun.

(1) Out of the dozen cookies, Chad _____ four and now there are _____ left.

(2) Which _____ does the needle point when you get on the scale to _____ yourself?

(3) It was a beautiful day with a pretty _____ sky and the wind _____ softly through the trees.

(4) The _____ of us went _____ the movies, _____.

(5) I _____ _____ - handed while my brother writes left-handed.

(6) After we had _____ the last game, we had only _____ more game before the championships.

(7) We were there _____ less than a week, as we stayed only _____ days.

(8) I was the only person in the _____ class with a _____ in my jacket sleeve.

(b) For each of these words, write its homophone and then write a short meaning for each.

(1) wait   (4) sent   (7) read   (10) by
(2) flu   (5) meet   (8) eye
(3) sew   (6) hear   (9) knot

(c) Use three of the word pairs in sentences.

8. Compound Caper

In the treasure chest are small words. Each of these words can be joined to another word in the chest to make compound words.

(a) Use the clues to write the twelve compound words.

    (1) not outside
    (2) a schedule of times
    (3) not outdoor
    (4) at a time still to come
    (5) a shelf that holds books
    (6) not inside
    (7) a snack that pops

    (8) a ball that you kick
    (9) a netted frame to walk on the snow
  (10) not indoor
  (11) where the chimney ends in a house
  (12) flat round cakes eaten with syrup

door fire snow in table side cakes pop
case book place time pan
foot ball corn out shoe some

(b) Write short clues for these compound words:

    (1) bedroom
    (2) highway
    (3) playground
    (4) downstairs
    (5) afternoon
    (6) airplane

9. Idioms

When we talk or write about our feelings, we sometimes use a descriptive group of words to tell what we mean. Like this:

Laura said she was all tied up in knots.

"I felt like I was going to fall apart," **said Ian.**

The first sentence tells how **nervous** Laura was. The second sentence describes how **upset** Ian was. These describing phrases are called **idioms**.

(a) Match each of these idioms with its meaning. Write the idioms in your notebook and beside each one write its meaning.

Idioms	Meanings
down in the dumps	nervous, scared
butterflies in your stomach	wait for a long time
under the weather	depressed, sad
all thumbs	in trouble
pigheaded	clumsy, awkward
hold your breath	ill, sick
simmer down	stubborn
up a tree	angry, furious
hit the ceiling	relax, calm yourself

(b) Choose five of the idioms. For each one, write a sentence or two about a time when **you** felt like that.

10. In the Early Days

When the first settlers came to Canada, they did not have many of the things we have today.

(a) Look carefully at the picture. Make a list of at least eight things that should **not** be in the picture.

(b) For five of the things you listed, write a sentence to explain what you think the settlers did instead of using that thing.

11. Kennings

Toe-warmers and **foot-holders** tell what socks and shoes are used for, but are funny ways of saying socks and shoes. Describing an ordinary thing this way instead of using a simple name is called a **kenning**. Here are some other kennings:

- A hat could be a head-house.
- A coat could be a body-protector.

(a) Make up kennings for each of these items:

(1) jeans	(5) scarf	(9) umbrella
(2) galoshes	(6) button	(10) belt
(3) pocket	(7) mittens	(11) sweater
(4) shoelaces	(8) sneakers	(12) bathing suit

(b) Choose five of your kennings and use each in a sentence. Pass your sentences to a friend to see if he or she can figure out what items you are describing.

12. Descriptions

We roasted marshmallows. Then we ate them.

OR

At our family picnic, we roasted marshmallows over an open, crackling fire. The sweet smell of the marshmallows filled the air. When they were swollen with dark crusty edges, we popped them into our mouths. The fluffy insides melted on our tongues. Yummy!

The second description sounds much more appetizing. The describing words make you almost see the fire, smell the air, hear the crackle of the fire, taste the marshmallows, and feel them melting on your tongue.

(a) Pick three of these or use your own ideas. Copy the chart and fill in as many columns as you can.

- cotton candy
- a ripe lemon
- a pickle
- a busy street
- a playground
- a peanut-butter sandwich

Looks	Sounds	Feels	Tastes	Smells

(b) For two of the things you have charted, write sentences that use the describing words you chose.

(c) Put the sentences together to create a descriptive paragraph.

13. Timely Words

(a) Find out more about time by solving this puzzle. Choose and write the time word that fits each clue.

Time Words

quarter century   centennial   century   weekly
bimonthly   semiannually biweekly   biennially
quarterly   bicentennial annually   monthly

(1) This word means four times a year.
(2) This word means every two months.
(3) This word means twice a year, or once every six months.
(4) This word means every two weeks.
(5) This word means every 200 years.
(6) This word means every two years.
(7) This word means once a month.
(8) This word means once a year.
(9) This word means 25 years.
(10) This word means every 100 years.
(11) This word means 100 years.
(12) This word means once a week.

(b) Choose any five of the time words. For each, write a sentence about an event that may happen then.

14. Guided Tours

You can use sentences to take people on a tour of a place. For example, a tour of your living room might start like this:

My living room is very big. The couch is along the wall to the right of the doorway. It has big, soft cushions so that you can curl up and read a book or watch TV. In front of the couch is a low wooden coffee table. There are magazines and a plant on top of it. On the right side of the couch is an old, over-stuffed easy chair. That chair is my cat's favourite place in the whole house!

(a) Write your own tour of a room in your house. Be sure to write the directions so that people will understand where each thing is. Make your tour interesting by using words that tell how you feel.

(b) Draw a picture of the room you described. Label all of the things in your picture.

15. Sports Dictionary

If someone wrote a dictionary just for hockey players, words like **skates**, **puck**, **score**, **stick**, and **face-off** would be in it.

(a) Complete the hockey player's dictionary. Add at least eight words to the list. Then, put all the words in alphabetical order and write the meaning beside each word.

(b) Think of your own favourite sport or choose one of the sports below. Make a player's dictionary. Write ten words that would go in your player's dictionary. Put the words in alphabetical order and beside each word write its meaning.

gymnastics   tennis   lacrosse   soccer
baseball   sailing   badminton   basketball

16. Secret Code

You have been left alone on a desert island. All you have with you are your clothes and a coded message. All of the vowels in the code are replaced by squares, and the other letters have moved.

A	B	C	D	E	F	G	H	I	J	K	L	M
■	A	B	C	■	D	E	F	■	G	H	I	J

N	O	P	Q	R	S	T	U	V	W	X	Y	Z
K	■	L	M	N	O	P	■	Q	R	S	T	U

Here is a message written in the code:

T ■ ■ / ■ N ■ / I ■ O P .

You are lost.

(a) Decode this message and write it in your notebook. (**Remember**: You have to decide which vowels are needed.)

I ■ ■ H / A ■ O ■ C ■ / P F ■ / A ■ O F ■ O . / C ■ C , T ■ ■
D ■ K C / ■ / A ■ ■ P / P F ■ N ■ ? / ■ D / K ■ P , / D ■ I I ■ R /
P F ■ / L ■ P F / A ■ P R ■ ■ K / P F ■ / P N ■ ■ O .
P F ■ P / ■ O / P F ■ / R N ■ K E / R ■ T . / N ■ K /
■ B N ■ O O / P F ■ / N ■ B H O / P ■ / P F ■ / R ■ I I . /
T ■ ■ / ■ N ■ / K ■ P / E ■ P P ■ K E / ■ K T / B I ■ O ■ N . /
T ■ ■ / J ■ O P / N ■ J ■ ■ K / ■ K / P F ■ / ■ O I ■ K C . /

(b) Write your own secret message using the code. Give it to a friend to decode.

17. The Five Senses

You can use words to tell how something tastes, looks, feels, sounds, or smells. For example:

(tastes)
the bitter lemon

(sounds)
the crashing cymbals

(looks)
the clear water

(smells)
the strong ammonia

(feels)
the slimy eel

(a) Write at least three sense words that tell how each of these things might look, feel, taste, sound, or smell.

   (1) a fire smells...
   (2) a peach tastes...and feels...
   (3) a monster looks...and sounds...
   (4) a bag of popcorn smells...and tastes...
   (5) a castle looks...
   (6) a ghost looks...and sounds...

(b) Choose two of the things you wrote sense words for and write three sentences to tell what you like or don't like about each. In your sentences, use the sense words you chose and add as many more as you can.

18. Word Trips

(a) Complete this word trip. Copy the boxes in your notebook and follow the arrows to fill in the spaces. Write a word you think of when you say the word in the box you just left.

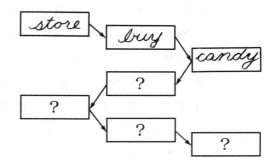

(b) Make three of your own word trips. You may start with these words or choose your own ideas. Make each of your word trips at least seven words long.

pet money fruit

(c) Pick a word trip and write a story that your word trip makes you think of.

19. Backward-Forward Magic

Some words can be read both backward and forward. For example:
dad, mom, tot, and sees

(a) Use the clues to write backward-forward words. When you are done, the letters in the pole will tell you the name for backward-forward words.

   (1) bird's chirp; rhymes with leap
   (2) Inuit's boat
   (3) equal height
   (4) past tense of done
   (5) midday
   (6) a task; rhymes with seed
   (7) instrument that uses radio waves to find unseen objects
   (8) songs sung by one person
   (9) name used to address a lady
 (10) more red

(b) Some words written backwards make another word.

ten backwards is net

Use eight of the backward-forward words below in sentences. Like this:

I hit the net ten times.

no	gulp	pals	reed	edit	live	step
yam	pit	was	top	raw	trap	mug

20. Sound Inventions

Some words sound like what they are describing. For example:

pop sounds like a balloon bursting

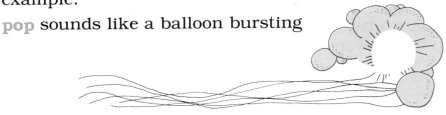

buzz sounds like a bee in the flowers

(a) Write each word in your notebook and beside it write three things it could be describing.

crunch	thump	plop	sizzle
swoosh	chatter	howl	squeak
jingle	grunt	flutter	clang

(b) Invent your own sound words. For example:

flump could be the sound of a pillow hitting the floor

ker-splunk could be the sound of a frog jumping into a pond

Write these things in your notebook. Beside each one make up a word that sounds like the thing.

thunder	wind	running shoes	horse
butterfly	fire	leaf	chalk

21. Animal Crossword

(a) Make an animal crossword puzzle. Write the name of an animal, fish, bird, or insect. Use a letter in that word to help make another animal word. Now use any letters in the two words to make a third animal word, and so on. The words go across or down. Like this:

```
            p
            o c t o p u s
            r             n
    l       c             a n t
d i n o s a u r           k
    o       p             e
    n       i
            n
            e
```

How many animal words can you add to these puzzles?

```
(1) c h e e t a h   (2) m                (3)           h
        i               o                              o
        g               n          z e b r a
        e           k a n g a r o o                    s
        r               e                              e
                        y
```

(b) Make your own crossword puzzle using as many animal words as you can. (**Hint**: You can make a bigger puzzle if you use some longer words like centipede or alligator.)

143

22. As Free as a Bird

When we describe people,
we sometimes compare
them to animals. Like this:

He was **as quiet as a mouse**.

(a) Choose the words from the group below that will
complete these comparisons. Write the completed
comparisons in your notebook.

(1) as _____ as a bee   (6) as _____ as a swan

(2) as _____ as a bug   (7) as _____ as a hornet

(3) as _____ as an ostrich   (8) as _____ as an owl

(4) as _____ as a peacock   (9) as _____ as a lark

(5) as _____ as a goose   (10) as _____ as a fox

mad   graceful   happy   snug   proud

silly   wise   sly   busy   shy

(b) We can compare people to other animals as well.
Complete these comparisons using other animal
names.

(1) as hungry as a. . .   (4) as light as a. . .

(2) as stubborn as a. . .   (5) as angry as a. . .

(3) as noisy as a. . .

(c) Make up four comparisons of your own. Use each one in
a sentence.

23. Diamond Poems

(a) Here is how you can
write a diamond poem
that looks like this:

land
rocky, flat
fields, cities, mountains
green, plush—blue, deep
waves, cool, drops
floating, clear
water

(1) Pick two things that
are opposites.

(2) Write one of the two things
on a line.

(3) On the next line write two words
that tell about the thing.

144

(4) On the next line write three words that tell about the thing.

(5) On the next line write two more words that remind you of the thing. Then write two words that remind you of its opposite.

(6) The next line has three words that tell about the opposite thing.

(7) The next line has only two words that describe the opposite.

(8) Finish the poem by writing the opposite.

(b) Write your own diamond poem. Choose one of these pairs of opposites or use your own ideas.

- sun—shade
- smooth—rocky
- night—day

24. A Gathering of Animals

Groups of animals have special names. Like this:

a colony of ants   a drove of cattle

(a) Unscramble the capital letters to find the name of each group of animals. (**Hint**: The scrambled word rhymes with the word printed like this.)

(1) Bees will form into a RAWMS.

(2) You cannot haggle with a GLAGEG of geese.

(3) Did you see the bird among the RHED of elephants.

(4) Hide when you see a REPID of lions.

(5) There is a rule among the COHOLS of fish.

(6) Raise a hand to the NDBA of gorillas.

(7) You'd better not touch the CHUCLT of chickens.

(8) Stand on the beam to see the EATM of horses.

(9) Be quiet when you walk around a CLOKF of sheep.

(b) The word skulk means "to sneak away." Why do you think skulk is a good name for a group of foxes? Make up your own names for these groups of animals.

(1) kittens   (3) snakes   (5) zebras   (7) mice

(2) monkeys   (4) rabbits   (6) frogs   (8) alligators

25. Hidden Forest

(a) Some of the names for trees are hiding in these sentences. Read the sentences carefully to find all twelve trees. As you find each name, write it beside the sentence number in your notebook. The first one is done for you.

willow	aspen	ash	maple
cherry	balsam	poplar	beech
cedar	pear	pine	hemlock

(1) Now I'll owe you only a quarter.
(2) Long ago, feathers were used as pens.
(3) Grandma, please come to visit us.
(4) In the panic her rye bread fell.
(5) Rob, Al, Sam, and Tom are pals.
(6) A bee chooses its flowers carefully.
(7) The matador faced a raging bull.
(8) We left them locked up in the cellar.
(9) I love to look at the mountaintop in early dawn.
(10) Did you pop Larry's balloon?
(11) If she was home today, I could play with her.
(12) The ape arrived at the zoo last week.

(b) Now hide six of these forest words in your own sentences. Exchange your sentences with a friend.

root   branch   pine   cone
leaves   blossom   birch   plant

26. Elemenno/LMNO

Play Elemenno. Pick some letters in a row from the alphabet. Choose words that start with those letters to make up interesting sports sentences. Like this:

L eagues   H ockey
M ight   I s
N ever   J ust
O ffer   K nowing
P layers   L ittle
Q uiet   M oves.
R est.

(a) Complete these Elemennos using imaginative words:

A ll   G oalies   Q uick
B aseball   H ide   R unners
C   ?   I   ?   S   ?
D   ?   J   ?   T   ?

(b) Make up three of your own Elemennos.

27. Pack Those Suitcases

Some words are like suitcases because they carry two or more words in one. For example:

splatter
blends **splash** and **sputter**

smog
blends **smoke** and **fog**

(a) Blend these words into suitcase words and write them in your notebook. The suitcase word meanings are given, and the number in the second column tells how many letters each suitcase word has.

Blended Words	Letters in Suitcase Word	Suitcase Word Meaning
(1) motorized + pedal bicycle	5	motorized bicycle
(2) motor car + parade	9	procession of automobiles
(3) bat + mash	4	to hit hard
(4) motor + hotel	5	hotel for motorists
(5) flame + glare	5	bright, unsteady light
(6) smack + mash	5	break in pieces
(7) breakfast + lunch	6	meal combining breakfast and lunch
(8) clap + crash	5	a loud noise
(9) news + broadcast	8	news on radio or TV
(10) travel + monologue	10	a talk or film about travel

(b) Invent your own suitcase words. Blend recess with lunch or trip with vacation. What do you get?

Make a list of five of your own suitcase words. Beside each, write the two blended words and the meaning of your suitcase words.

28. 👁 ♡ a Rebus

A **rebus** is a little picture that can be used in place of a word in a sentence. Here is a sentence that uses rebuses:

My 🦷 are in my 👄 .

This sentence means:

My teeth are in my mouth.

(a) Rewrite this story putting in the words where you see rebuses:

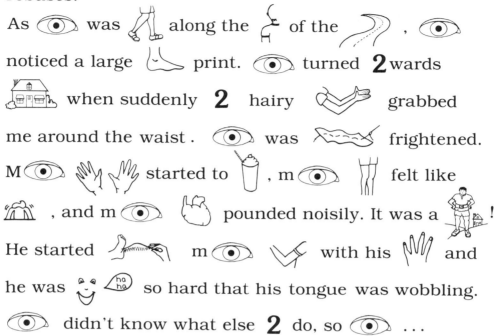

As 👁 was 🦵 along the 🦴 of the 🛣, 👁 noticed a large 🦶 print. 👁 turned **2**wards 🏠 when suddenly **2** hairy 💪 grabbed me around the waist. 👁 was 🥓 frightened. M👁 🖐🖐 started to 🥤, m👁 🦵 felt like 🏔, and m👁 💗 pounded noisily. It was a 🧑‍🌾! He started 👣 m👁 🦵 with his 🖐 and he was 😀 ha ha so hard that his tongue was wobbling. 👁 didn't know what else **2** do, so 👁 ...

(b) Finish the story using rebuses in place of some of the words.

29. A Field of Words

To make a word web you write down a word. Then you write two words it makes you think of. Then you write two words you think of for each of the two words you just wrote. Here is the beginning of a word web on farming:

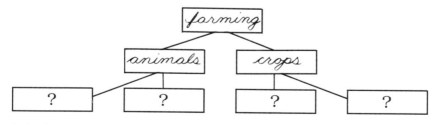

(a) Copy the web and complete it using your own words.

(b) Now make a word web for each of these words. How long can you make your word webs?

(1) pets   (3) food   (5) games

(2) sports   (4) trees   (6) shops

30. A Summer Haiku

A special kind of poem that tells about nature comes from Japan. It is called a **haiku** (hī′ kū). A haiku uses only three lines and seventeen word parts. Here is a haiku about summer:

Sunshine all around	5 word parts
Soft green grass under my feet	7 word parts
Summer is the best	5 word parts.

(a) Complete these haikus about summer. Remember that the last line uses only five word parts.

Swimming in the lake
Cool lemonade in the park
———————

❖ ❖ ❖

Long, hot days to play
Warm breeze caressing my face
———————

(b) Write two of your own summer haikus.

Word List

Word List

Word List

153

Mini-Dictionary

Sound Key

The **Sound Code** in brackets after each word in this dictionary tells how you say the word. The different sounds that the letters and symbols have are shown in the examples below.

Alphabet Letter	Sound Symbol	Example
a	a	apple, pizza
	ā	ape, cake
	ȧ	arm, car
ch	ch	chin, watch
e	e	bed, elbow
	ē	eagle, feet
f or ph	f	foot, graph
g	g	go, great
	j	gem, edge
i	i	ink, it
	ī	line, tie
ng	ng	singer, ring
o	o	sock, hot
	ō	open, toe
	ȯ	ball, off
oi or oy	oi	oil, boy
ou or ow	ou	out, owl
q	kw	quiet, square
sh	sh	she, shoe
th	th	thin, both
	͞TH	that, mother
u	u	cup, thumb
	u̇	foot, put
	ū	two, rule
wh	hw	wheel, whistle
x	ks	six, exit
	gz	exam

154

Special sounds ....ur ....earth, fur, bird

yū ....you, music

zh ....treasure, measure

(Schwa sound) ....ə ....a as in alone

e as in taken

i as in pencil

o as in lemon

u as in circus

Short Forms Used in This Dictionary

adj.   adjective
       (describing word)

adv.   adverb
       (describing word)

n.   noun
       (naming word)

v.   verb
       (action word)

pl.   plural
       (more than one)

conj. conjunction
       (joining word)

pron. pronoun
       (naming word)

pref. prefix
       (word beginning)

A

answer (an′ sər) *v*. 1. to reply to a question or a letter. 2. to respond: *He answered the phone*. *n*. 1. the reply to a question or a letter: *She wrote a brief answer*. 2. a gesture or motion in response: *His nod was the only answer he gave*. (**answered**, **answering**)

aren't (ȧrnt) short for **are not**.

automobile (ȯ′ tə mə bēl′) *n*. a motor car.

B

1 **batter** (bat′ ər) *v*. to hit and cause to bruise or break: *He battered down the door*. (**battered**, **battering**)

2 **batter** (bat′ ər) *n*. a thick liquid mixture used as the base for baking or cooking: *Pancakes are made from batter*.

broad (brȯd) *adj*. 1. very wide: *He has broad shoulders*. 2. large; a lot of: *She has broad experience in teaching*. 3. general; not detailed: *They have broad ideas*. 4. clear; full: *He stole the car in broad daylight*.

C

can't (kant) short for **cannot**.

castle (kas′ əl) *n*. a big building or buildings where royalty lives; a palace: *The queen lived in a beautiful castle*.

Mini-Dictionary

155

chase (chās) *v.* 1. to follow after to catch; to hunt: *Dogs chase cats.* 2. to drive away: *Cats chase birds from a garden.* 3. follow; to go after: *He chased the kite.* *n.* going after: *a car chase.* (**chased, chasing**)

closet (kloz′ it) *n.* a cupboard or small room used for storing things: *She hung her jacket in the hall closet.*

club (klub) *n.* 1. a thick stick used as a weapon. 2. a bat or stick used when playing some games: *a golf club.* 3. a group of people who meet to enjoy some interest together: *He joined the science club.* 4. a playing card with a black design shaped like a three-leaf clover. *v.* to hit with a club. (**clubbed, clubbing**)

couldn't (kůd′ ənt) short for **could not.**

cousin (kuz′ ən) *n.* a child of one's parent's brother or sister; one's aunt's or uncle's child.

D

didn't (did′ ənt) short for **did not.**

dinosaur (dī′ nə sor) *n.* any of a group of reptiles that lived millions of years ago.

doesn't (duz′ ənt) short for **does not.**

E

easy (ēz′ ē) *adj.* 1. not hard to do: *It was an easy puzzle.* 2. giving comfort: *She sat in the easy chair.* 3. smooth; not awkward: *He has an easy way of speaking.* (**easier, easiest**)

F

family (fam′ ə lē) *n.* 1. parents or their children. 2. all of one's relatives. 3. the children of a mother and father. 4. a group of related people. 5. a group of related plants or animals: *Penguins and pelicans belong to the bird family.* (*pl.* **families**)

floor (flȯr) *n.* 1. the part of a room that is walked or stood on; the flat surface or bottom of anything: *the ocean floor.* 2. a storey of a building: *the fifth floor.* *v.* to put down a floor: *We will floor the kitchen with tiles.*

forget (fȯr get′) *v.* to not remember: *I hope I don't forget my books.*

forgot (fȯr got′) *v.* past tense of **forget**: *I forgot my books at home.*

G

ghost (gōst) *n.* 1. the spirit of a dead person. 2. anything pale or shadowy: *Are you ill? You look like a ghost.*

H

hadn't (had′ ənt) short for **had not.**

hasn't (haz′ ənt) short for **has not.**

haven't (hav′ ənt) short for **have not.**

J

job (job) *n.* 1. work; what one does for a living: *My job is to paint.* 2. work done for payment. 3. what one has to do: *Taking out the garbage is my job around the house.*

K

kitchen (kich′ ən) *n.* the room where food is prepared and cooked.

L

loving (luv′ ing) *adj.* being affectionate: *Our cat is very loving towards us.*

M

1 **match** (mach) *n.* a short, thin piece of wood with a special tip that will catch fire when rubbed against a special surface: *He used a match to light the candles.* (*pl.* **matches**)

2 **match** (mach) *n.* 1. someone or something equal to or very much alike someone or something else: *Twins are a perfect match. That couch and chair are a good match.* 2. a game or contest: *a tennis match.*

monster (mon′ stər) *n.* 1. a plant or an animal that is not like what is usually seen: *A fire-breathing mouse is a monster.* 2. an imaginary creature.

move (mūv) *v.* 1. to change the location of: *Please move over.* 2. to change the place where one lives: *Sally moved away.* 3. in motion: *He moves around a lot when he dances.* *n.* 1. movement: *Stand still, don't make a move.* (**moved**, **moving**).

N

nearly (nēr′ lē) *adv.* 1. almost: *Recess is nearly over.* 2. closely:

As nearly as I can tell, the game will be over by noon.

O

others (uth′ ərz) *pron.* 1. some different, additional, or remaining persons or things: *He helps others. I have three pencils here, but the others are over there.*

P

picnic (pik′ nik) *n.* a meal eaten outdoors: *We ate sandwiches at out family picnic.* *v.* to eat a meal outdoors: *We like to picnic in the park.* (**picnicked**, **picnicking**)

police (pə lēs′) *n.* the men and women whose job it is to keep law and order: *The police arrested the thief.* *v.* to guard or keep order: *They will police the streets.* (**policed**, **policing**)

Q

quickly (kwik′ lē) *adv.* to hurry; to move fast: *She ran home quickly.*

R

raise (rāz) *v.* 1. to put up; to lift: *Raise your hand.* 2. to increase in amount, degree, and so on: *The store raised the price of milk.* 3. to grow or breed: *We raise pigs on our farm.* 4. to bring up: *Your parents raise you.* 5. to call attention to; to mention: *She raised an important question.* *n.* an increase in pay or wages: *Her boss gave her a raise in pay.* (**raised**, **raising**)

re- (rē) *pref.* 1. once more, again: *recount, recover, recycle.* 2. back: *repay, rebound, refund.*

Mini-Dictionary

S

size (sīz) *n.* 1. the amount of space something takes up: *The two boxes are the same size.* 2. one of a series of amounts or measures: *My shirt size is small.*

special (spesh′ əl) *adj.* 1. different from others; not the same: *You need a special wheel to fit that bike.* 2. unusual; not ordinary: *She has special powers.* 3. held in high regard; valued greatly: *Swimming holds special appeal to me.* 4. for a particular purpose, person, or thing: *This is my special dress for holidays.* *n.* 1. a featured product in a store: *a special on books.* 2. a TV show not part of regular programming: *an Easter special.*

T

1 **tear** (tēr) *n.* a drop of water that comes out of the eye: *He was in tears when he hurt his arm.*

2 **tear** (tār or ter) *v.* 1. to pull apart: *She will tear the letter in half.* 2. to make by pulling apart: *He tore a hole in the paper.* 3. to cut or wound: *She tore her foot on a nail.* (**tore, torn, tearing**)

U

unless (un les′) *conj.* except; if not: *We will go tomorrow unless it snows.*

upstairs (up′ stārz′) *adv.* 1. up the stairs: *We went upstairs.* 2. on an upper floor: *She works upstairs.* *adj.* of or on an upper floor: *He sat in the upstairs bedroom.* *n.* the upper floor or floors: *Our house does not have an upstairs.*

V

visiting (viz′ it ing) *v.* to go or come to see: *We will be visiting you next week.*

W

wasn't (wuz′ ənt or woz′ ənt) short for **was not.**

weren't (wurnt or wernt) short for **were not.**

X

x-ray (eks′ rā) *n.* an invisible ray used to take pictures of the inside of the body. (*pl.* **x-rays**). *v.* to take a picture using invisible rays: *The doctor can x-ray you to see what's wrong.* (**x-rayed, x-raying**)

Y

yours (yūrz or yorz) *pron.* belonging to you: *This hat is mine, but that one is yours.*

Z

zipper (zip′ ər) *n.* a sliding fastener: *The zipper on his coat was stuck.*

Mini-Dictionary

158

Mini-Thesaurus

		Synonyms and Related Words	Antonyms and Related Words
delight	n.	pleasure, enjoyment *Rel.*: satisfaction, amusement, thrill	sadness *Rel.*: depression
float	v.	hold up (as on water) *Rel.*: risen, lighten, sail, swim	sink *Rel.*: submerge, settle, immerse
forms	n.	shapes, figures, molds *Rel.*: models, frames, profiles, outlines	
	v.	makes, creates, shapes, molds	disfigures *Rel.*: break, ruin, dismantle, take apart, destroy
happy	adj.	glad, pleased, joyful, merry *Rel.*: glowing, radiant, gleeful, amused, smiling, cheerful	unhappy, sad *Rel.*: depressed
hunting	v.	searching for, tracking, seeking, pursuing *Rel.*: stalking, chasing, going after, probing, inquiring	
living	v.	alive, having life *Rel.*: breathing	dead
passed	v.	1. gone, gone by *Rel.*: departed, expired, dead, dated 2. succeeded, did well *Rel.*: correct, picked, elected, selected	2. failed

		Synonyms and Related Words	Antonyms and Related Words
path	*n.*	road, trail, track *Rel.*: route, course, walkway, sidewalk	
pushed	*v.*	1. pressed, shoved, thrust 2. urged, encouraged, coaxed, pressured	1. held 2. discouraged
safe	*adj.* *n.*	1. unhurt, unharmed, out of danger *Rel.*: secure, protected, guarded, cautious 2. a vault *Rel.*: strongbox, locker	1. dangerous, harmed, hurt *Rel.*: unprotected, unguarded
scared	*adj.*	afraid, frightened *Rel.*: fearful	brave, unafraid

Mini-Thesaurus